THE FIVE TIBETAN RITES

Ancient Anti-Aging Secrets of The Five Tibetan Rites

THE FIVE TIBETAN RITES
Ancient Anti-Aging Secrets of The Five Tibetan Rites

Electronically composed and printed in Australia.

The edited sections and advice given in this book are not intended to replace or supersede professional medical advice. If you have any serious medical or psychological problems, you should consult your physician before undertaking these exercises or dietary recommendations. Neither the author nor the publisher can be held responsible for claims resulting from information contained in this book.

UnMind Pty Ltd
PO Box 818
NSW 2107
Australia

www.T5T.com

Paperback ISBN: 978-0-9870703-8-8
eBook ISBN: 978-0-9870703-0-2

Cover Design: Toby Andrews
Interior Design: Lazar Kackarovski

THE FIVE TIBETAN RITES

Ancient Anti-Aging Secrets of The Five Tibetan Rites

by

Carolinda Witt
& Peter Kelder

Includes

The Eye of Revelation (1939 and 1946 Editions)
by Peter Kelder

Additional practice information, tips, and advice
by Carolinda Witt
T5T Five Tibetan Rites Teacher
Founder and Developer of T5T®

TABLE OF CONTENTS

INTRODUCTION

This book is a combination of Peter Kelder's classic story, *The Eye of Revelation*, written in 1939 and updated in 1946, together with additional practice information and tips from my twenty-one years of teaching the Five Tibetan Rites.

The Eye of Revelation tells the story of a Westerner known only as 'Colonel Bradford,' who discovered a secret sect of monks living in a remote Tibetan monastery who were remarkably healthy and youthful despite their advanced years.

Bradford lived and studied with the monks for several years, where they taught him their secret to the fountain of youth. He brought this information back to the West, where it became known as 'The Five Tibetan Rites of Rejuvenation' – a daily ritual of five yoga-like movements, a breathing technique, and some simple spiritual practices involving vocalized sound and mental techniques.

Several books on the subject have been written since, including my own, *The Illustrated Five Tibetan Rites*, but the source of every book on the subject is Peter Kelder's, *The Eye of Revelation*.

Thanks to the generosity of antiquarian bookseller and collector Jerry Watt (RIP), who granted me special permission to use the unadulterated text from his rare editions of *The*

Eye of Revelation - you are about to read Kelder's own words without amendments, additions, or interpretations by anyone else. There are only three known remaining copies of the 1939 edition in the world, and Jerry owned one of them. He also owned the only known copy of the 1946 edition, which contains additional information left out of the first.

I have combined these two editions together in this book, along with tips and insights from my many years of teaching The Five Tibetan Rites.

I began teaching the Rites in 2000 and have taught over 50,000 people since. My experiences led me to develop a way for people of all ages and varying levels of fitness to learn the Rites, which I call 'T5T®' — short for 'The Five Tibetans.'

There isn't the space to include everything I learned in this book or to outline the step-by-step process I teach in T5T. However, I have added additional information and suggested some actions to avoid when learning the Rites. I hope you find it useful.

HERE'S WHAT I LEARNED FROM PRACTICING, THEN TEACHING THE RITES

I learned 'The Five Tibetan Rites of Rejuvenation' from a friend (a teacher of the Rites) in 2000 and have practiced them almost every day since. They have seen me through all sorts of ups and downs in my life since then, and I know I'll never give them up. I call them "the rod of iron inside me around which the chaos of life revolves." A strong statement, I know, but let me tell you why.

When my friend persuaded me to learn the Rites, I was very cynical, particularly after she told me they would fix 'everything.' She was referring to my early menopausal symptoms of hot flushes, emotional fluctuations, foggy mind, unusual fatigue, empty nest syndrome, and loss of meaning and purpose. It was a long list, and I thought she was kidding.

I learned the Rites and started practicing them on my own, building up repetitions as recommended. Within two days, I experienced a significant (almost hyper) energy boost, which took a whole day to settle down. My night was restless, but I awoke feeling surprisingly fresh and eager to begin some of the tasks I had been putting off due to fatigue and procrastination. I seemed to have this well of energy that never depleted, and before I knew it, several tasks were reaching completion. It felt like I had emerged from a thick fog. When I began teaching the Rites, I realized that these great early experiences were common.

An initial detox effect can occur, too, as the nervous, circulatory, respiratory and life-energy systems of the body are stimulated by practicing the Rites. Any symptoms usually settle down within a week or two. You'll learn more about these later in the book.

I noticed that my general wellbeing and energy had improved considerably, and I looked forward to practicing the Rites every day. I began to plan exciting new directions in my life. Best of all, my hot flushes, which used to leave me with swimming pools in my navel at night, calmed right down. Whether this was due, or partly due, to the Rites is unknown, but I am certain they contributed.

Around six months into my practice, my family experienced the loss of someone close to us in a tragic accident. It was a terrible time, but I discovered my daily practice of the Rites kept me strong and centered and helped me deal with a difficult situation in a more balanced fashion. It was then that I realized how important the Rites had become to me mentally, physically, and emotionally.

My friend asked me to go into business with her running 'Five Tibetan Rites' workshops in Sydney, Australia. I agreed, and we were very successful, with many people participating in our workshops.

AS A TEACHER

We taught the Rites exactly as Kelder described, and people got great benefits, but a small percentage of students developed lower back or neck pain. On the other hand, people who were fit and had good body-mind awareness were generally fine as they knew how to exercise safely.

I wanted to stop this pattern from occurring at all, so I consulted with a wide variety of health practitioners (physiotherapists, osteopaths, chiropractors, occupational health practitioners, Pilates, Iyengar yoga, and Feldenkrais instructors) to discover the cause of these problems and how to fix them.

Let's face it; our modern Western lifestyle is very different from that of the monks described in *The Eye of Revelation*. They lived in the steep Himalayas, and walking around those mountains would have kept them fit. Their whole lifestyle, from food production to the simplest daily tasks, was menial and ensured they remained physically active.

All of the health practitioners consulted had concerns about the over-bending in the lower back and neck, as illustrated and described in *The Eye of Revelation*, and made useful suggestions. Because I wanted to retain the original integrity and benefits of the original Rites but make them safer for most people to practice, I tried their ideas out in the living laboratory of my classrooms.

A simple and effective method of learning the Rites (T5T) soon developed and provided students followed the program and didn't exert themselves; the incidents of lower back and neck pain all but disappeared. However, those students with a history of back or neck pain or injury should consult their qualified health practitioner.

By combining core strength development with the Rites in a series of ten steps, T5T takes you from beginner level through to intermediate, then advanced level and beyond. These ten steps coincide with the instructions of the monks, to begin with just 3 repetitions in your first week, then add 2 per week until you are doing the required 21 repetitions in ten weeks' time.

These steps develop strength and flexibility from the inside out, and you should make sure you perform the advanced levels only when your body is ready. T5T avoids strain and emphasizes a pleasurable learning experience.

The Eye of Revelation is a wonderful story about the discovery of the monks and their anti-aging secrets, written in the rather magical language of the times. I am sure you will enjoy it.

There is a questionnaire at the end of the book. It will help you decide whether to learn the Rites from a qualified yoga or Pilates teacher, by the T5T method, or from the simple instructions outlined in this book.

If you are an experienced yoga or Pilates practitioner, remember to keep your spine 'long and strong' to avoid compression.

I wish you a long and happy practice.

Kind regards,

Carolinda Witt

Note

1. The text in this document has been faithfully reproduced from the actual scans of the original 1939 and 1946 versions of *The Eye of Revelation*. The grammar, punctuation, and spelling have not been altered accordingly.

2. The intention of this book is to provide you with the *authentic* words of Kelder, exactly as he wrote them in 1939 and updated them in 1946. As a teacher of the Rites for over 21 years, I have shared some information which I am sure you will find useful – but if you wish to learn the T5T method, you have a number of options to choose from; online training, illustrated book, DVD and T5T instructors in various locations. See the *back of this book* for details.

3. My comments, tips, and advice have been written in this font to distinguish them from the original.

"**T5T** is an incredible and powerful program. It turns back the clock. It increases your energy, mental clarity, and focus. It reduces stress and improves strength and flexibility. It is capable of restoring your passion and zest for life if you let it. I highly recommend it for anyone willing to improve their life."

~ John Gray ~
Author of *Men are from Mars, Women are from Venus*

THE BENEFITS OF THE FIVE TIBETAN RITES

1

The reasons why people learn and practice the Rites:

Attracted to the anti-aging benefits of the Rites.

Have noticed the first signs of aging and want to do whatever they can to stop-the-clock.

To increase their energy levels, mental agility and focus.

Want a simple, daily routine that improves motivation, mood and purpose.

To maintain a regular exercise routine, and adopt a healthier lifestyle.

Improve strength and flexibility.

Lead busy lives, and want a form of exercise that fits into their daily routine. Takes just 10 to 15 minutes per day to practice once learned.

Strengthen their back to reduce back-ache or rehabilitate an injury (with doctor's approval.)

Like the idea of practicing yoga, but don't have the time or perhaps desire to attend classes.

Can be done anywhere, at any time. No special equipment or facilities needed.

The typical benefits people receive from doing the Rites vary from person to person. For some, the effects are dramatic, and for others, the improvements they notice at the beginning soon become part of their normal physiology. Others may not experience much of a change at all but describe a strong sense that the Rites are improving their health and vitality.

The cumulative benefits seem to continue, and there are many people in their 70's to '90s still doing the Rites after 20 years or more of practice.

Mention needs to be made here of the proliferation of claims for the benefits of practicing the Rites that have been made over the internet. This is primarily due to internet marketers selling a version of *The Eye of Revelation* book on a commission basis. They have no experience of teaching the Rites and may not even practice them personally. They tend to exaggerate the benefits of the Rites, with the more unscrupulous among them proclaiming them as a sort of miracle cure. Unfortunately, this approach dilutes the Rites' credibility, as people's expectations become sky-high, and they soon become disillusioned.

People are led to believe that the Rites will completely halt their aging, help them lose enormous amounts of weight, and fix their cancer, heart disease, fibroid cysts, and numerous other serious health conditions. As a result, anything short of a miracle is therefore seen as somewhat ho-hum.

In fact, the monks who developed the Rites didn't describe specific benefits – they simply stated that the specific purpose of the Rites is to regain health, youth, and vitality:

> "The body has seven centers, which, in English, could be called Vortexes. These are kind of magnetic centers. They revolve at great speed in the healthy body, but when slowed down – well, that is just another name for old age, ill-health, and senility. The quickest way to regain health, youth, and vitality is to start these magnetic centers spinning again. There are but five practices that will do this. Any one of them will be helpful, but all five are required to get glowing results. These five exercises are really not exercises at all, in the physical culture sense. The Lamas think of them as 'Rites,' and so instead of calling them exercises or practices, we too shall call them 'Rites.'"

~ **Peter Kelder**, author of *The Eye of Revelation*.

While it is important to have realistic expectations, the power of belief (or faith) is still a vital force. Colonel Bradford himself said you need to invest a strong amount of faith and belief in the Rites to maximize their benefit. If you think old, you behave old, for example.

Most people are familiar with the medical use of placebos. A common practice is to give a patient an inert sugar pill, telling him/her that this will improve their condition. They are not told that the pill is a placebo. The patient's belief does indeed have a therapeutic effect, improving the condition it was intended for.

WHAT KIND OF BENEFITS CAN YOU EXPECT?

The following list has been compiled from the testimonials and evidence given by the many thousands of students who have attended T5T workshops or learned the Rites through my books or DVD.

A significant increase in energy - more the endurance type of energy as opposed to the revved-up caffeine type of energy. You feel like you can keep going and going.

Feel calmer and less stressed - your buttons simply don't get pushed as easily anymore.

Develop significant mental clarity with razor-sharp focus.

Feel stronger, more flexible, and less stiff.

Enjoy seeing muscles appear on your arms, stomachs, hips, legs, and backs. Good for toning flabby arms, and tightening the abdomen.

Sleep better. Some people have more vivid dreams.

Overall improvement in your health, don't seem to catch colds, etc., as often. Helps with depression and anxiety - lifts mood and improves well-being. More centered and at peace.

Improved self-discipline and sense of purpose.

Feel younger and more powerful.

Improved breathing - deeper, slower, and more conscious.

Increased levels of Qi (chi, prana, life-energy).

Better posture.

Develops good core strength, which provides a strong foundation for any other form of exercise or modern living.

Some people lose weight; most find it easier to control weight and desire healthier foods.

Improved digestion and elimination.

Helps with the transition and symptoms of menopause.

Helps with the symptoms of menstruation.

Improved libido.

Many people also claim the Rites have made significant improvements to their health conditions. You can read about these on my T5T.com website under *Testimonials*. Each person's real name is provided.

ANTI-STRESS, CALM & RELAXATION

The Five Tibetans help you handle stress better. When you practice them, you'll notice you become calmer and more centered. You become less volatile as your buttons don't get pushed as easily, and you're more able to live in the present moment instead of constantly rushing for some imagined future event. This increased awareness makes for a happier, more fulfilling life.

Today many people exercise with music blaring, watching TV, or even reading books as they cycle away at the gym. With The Five Tibetans, it is best to consider your practice as a meditation in motion. That doesn't mean you have to do it really slowly (unless you want to) - it means remaining conscious and present in your body while practicing the movements. Increasing your focus and attention in this way is very calming and centering.

USE BREATHING TO CALM YOUR MIND

A simple way of calming yourself is to breathe slower and deeper. Even if your mind is racing ahead with lists and deadlines, simply slow your breathing rate, and your mind will slow too.

Remember, it is now proven without any doubt that reducing stress enhances sleeping patterns, improves health, and decreases anxiety, depression, and anger.

2

HEALTH CONSIDERATIONS

Whenever you begin a new exercise program, there are always health considerations to take into account. The information in this section is by no means comprehensive, and you should not substitute it for the direct advice of your doctor or health care provider.

If you feel any unusual discomfort or pain when you begin the Rites, stop practicing the exercises immediately, and discuss the situation with your qualified health-care provider. If you have had a previous injury or are suffering from one at the moment, you must check with your health practitioner to ensure that the Rites will not aggravate your injury. Also, if you have a history of knee, shoulder, back, or neck injuries, it is always advisable to consult a qualified medical professional before attempting any of the postures.

PREGNANCY

It's important to note that the Rites are not intended for pregnant women, as this is not the best time for you to begin a new workout program, particularly without the advice of a qualified health or fitness professional. If you are pregnant and have already been practicing yoga or Pilates regularly, you should discuss this program with a qualified prenatal yoga or Pilates Instructor, as modifications or alterations may be possible. Some of these exercises are not recommended, however, particularly in late-term. Once your baby is delivered, you'll find that the exercises are an excellent way to get yourself back into shape, and they can be done while the baby sleeps – or at a time that suits you.

You should consult your physician before commencing the Rites if you have any of the following serious medical or psychological problems:

- Heat valve problems
- Enlarged heart
- Recent heart attack
- High or low blood pressure
- Cancer
- Meniere's disease
- Vertigo
- Multiple sclerosis
- Parkinson's disease
- Seizure disorders
- Mental illness

Also, consult your physician if you are taking drugs that cause dizziness, if you have had recent abdominal or chest surgery, or if you suffer from any of the following:

- Hernia
- Ulcers
- Hyperthyroidism
- Chronic fatigue syndrome
- Disc disease
- Fibromyalgia
- Severe arthritis of the spine

- Carpal tunnel syndrome
- Lower back injury
- Retinal or eye pressure (glaucoma)

FOREWORD BY THE ORIGINAL PUBLISHERS

*T*he *Eye of Revelation* is truly a revelation. It reveals to you information which has been known and used by men in far-distant lands for more than 25 centuries, but which is now available to you for the first time. It is information which has been thoroughly tried and tested. Information that will stem the tide of premature old age with its attendant weaknesses and senility. This is information for which Ponce de Leon, and thousands of others down through the ages, would have given all they possessed.

The Eye of Revelation will often produce remarkable mental and physical changes within a month. So much so, in fact, that one gains new hope and enthusiasm, with which to carry on. However, the greatest results come after the tenth week. When you stop to consider that the average person has endured his afflictions from 20 to 30 years, to obtain gratifying results in such a short time as weeks sounds almost miraculous.

As long as you live and practice *The Eye of Revelation* you will get more and still more gratifying results.

Most Important: The information given in *The Eye of Revelation* was, for centuries, confined strictly to men. Now, to the surprise and delight of all concerned, it has been found that women, too, get equally beneficial and amazing results.

Now, man or woman, can go on to grand and glorious things, regardless of environment or circumstances.

Get started at once on the marvellous work of youthification, and may success, health, energy, power, vigor, virility, and life dog your footsteps forever.

COLONEL BRADFORD'S GREAT DISCOVERY – PART ONE

One afternoon I dropped into the Travelers Club to escape a sudden shower, and while seated in an easy chair I fell into conversation with a most interesting old gentleman; one who, although I did not know it then, was destined to change the whole course of my life. I call him an old man for that is exactly what he was. In his late sixties, he looked every year his age. He was thin and stooped, and when he walked leaned heavily on his cane.

It developed that he was a retired British army officer, who had seen service in the diplomatic corps of the Crown. There were few accessible places on the globe to which Colonel Bradford, as I shall call him, although that was not his true name, had not, at some time or other in his life, paid a visit. Warming under my attention he related incidents in his travels which were highly entertaining. Needless to say, I spent an interesting afternoon listening to him. This was some years ago. We met often after that and got along famously. Many evenings, either at his quarters or at mine, we discussed and discoursed until long past midnight.

It was on one of these occasions I became possessed of a feeling that Colonel Bradford wanted to tell me something of importance. Something close to his heart which was difficult for him to talk about. By using all the tact and diplomacy at my command I succeeded in making him understand that I should be happy to help him in any way possible, and that if he cared to tell me what was on his mind I would keep it in strict confidence. Slowly at first, and then with increased trust he began to talk.

While stationed in India some years ago, Colonel Bradford, from time to time, came in contact with wandering natives from the remote fastnesses of the country. He heard many interesting tales of the life and customs of the country. One story, which interested him strangely, he heard quite a number of times, and always from natives who inhabited a particular district. Those from other districts never seemed to have heard this story.

It concerned a group of Lamas or Tibetan priests who, apparently, had discovered "The Fountain of Youth." The natives told of old men who had mysteriously regained health and vigor, strength and virility shortly after entering a certain lamasery; but where this particular place was none seemed exactly to know.

Like so many other men, Colonel Bradford had become old at 40, and had not been getting any younger as the years rolled by. Now the more he heard this tale of "The Fountain of Youth" the more he became convinced that such a place and such men actually existed. He began to gather information on directions, character of the country, climate, and various other data that might help him locate the spot; for from then on there dwelt in the back of his mind a desire to find this "Fountain of Youth."

This desire, he told me, had now grown so powerful that he had determined to return to India and start in earnest a quest for the retreat of the young-old men; and he wanted me to go with him. Frankly, by the time he had finished telling me this fantastic story I, too, was convinced of its truth, and was half-tempted to join him, but I finally decided against it.

Soon he departed, and I consoled myself for not going with the thought that perhaps one should be satisfied to grow old gracefully; that perhaps the Colonel was wrong in trying to get more out of life than was vouchsafed to other men. And yet - a Fountain of Youth!!! What a thrilling idea it was! For his own sake I hoped that the old Colonel might find it.

Months passed. In the press of every-day affairs Colonel Bradford and his "Shangri-La" had grown dim in my memory, when one evening on returning to my apartment, there was a letter in the Colonel's own handwriting. He was still alive! The letter seemed to have been written in joyous desperation. In it he said that in spite of maddening delays and set-backs he actually was on the verge of finding the "Fountain." He gave no address.

It was more months before I heard from him again. This time he had good news. He had found the "Fountain of Youth"! Not only that, but he was bringing it back to the States with him, and would arrive within the next two months. Practically four years had elapsed since I had last seen the old man. Would he have changed any, I wondered? He was older, of course, but perhaps no balder, although his stoop might have increased a little. Then the startling idea came to me that perhaps this "Fountain of Youth" might really have helped him. But in my mind's eye I could not picture him differently than I had seen him last, except perhaps a little older.

One evening I decided to stay at home by myself and catch up on my reading, maybe write a few letters. I had finally settled down to comfortable reading when the telephone rang.

"A Colonel Bradford to see you, sir," said the desk clerk,

"Send him up," I shouted. In a short time a rap was heard on the door. I opened it in haste. For a moment I stared, and then with dismay I saw that this was not the Colonel Bradford I was hoping to see, but a much younger man.

Noting my surprise he said, "Weren't you expecting me?"

"No," I confessed. "I thought it would he an old friend of mine, a Colonel Bradford."

"I came to see you about Colonel Bradford, the man you were expecting," he answered.

"Come in," I invited.

"Allow me to introduce myself," said the stranger, entering. "My name is Bradford."

"Oh, you are Colonel Bradford's son," I exclaimed. "I have often heard him speak of you so often. You resemble him somewhat."

"No, I am not my son," he returned. "I am none other than your old friend, Colonel Bradford, the old man who went away to the Himalayas."

I stood in incredulous amazement at his statement. Then it slowly dawned upon me that this really was the Colonel Bradford whom I had known; but what a change had taken place in his appearance. Instead of the stooped, limping, sallow old gentleman with a cane, he was a tall, straight, ruddy-complexioned man in the prime of life.[1] Even his hair, which had grown back, held only a trace of grey.[2]

> (1) *The Rites improve your posture. They strengthen your back and abdominal muscles so you can hold yourself erect. If you make a conscious decision to remove 'old people mannerisms' from yourself, like stooping, slumping, dithering, etc., you'll feel more energetic, and people will say how much younger you look. You'll feel it too.*

(2) *I have only once observed a mild change in hair color. The sideburns of one of my students appeared to have darkened after several months of practice. Going from completely grey to completely dark is probably unrealistic, and if it happened regularly would be reported on the front page news. Bradford also recommended the use of fresh, unsalted butter massaged into the scalp to stimulate hair growth, which you'll read more about later.*

My enthusiasm and curiosity knew no bounds. Soon I was plying him with questions in rapid-fire order until he threw up his hands.

"Wait, wait," he protested, laughingly. "I shall start at the beginning and tell you all that has happened." And this he proceeded to do.

Upon arriving in India the Colonel started directly for the district in which lived the natives who had told of "The Fountain of Youth." Fortunately, he knew quite a bit of their language. He spent a number of months there, making friends with the people and picking up all the information he could about the Lamasery he sought. It was a long, slow process, but his shrewdness and persistence finally brought him to the coveted place he had heard about so often, but only half-believed existed.

Colonel Bradford's account of what transpired after being admitted to the Lamasery sounded like a fairy tale. I only wish that time and space permitted me to set down here all of his experiences; the interesting practices of the Lamas, their culture, and their utter indifference to the work-a-day world. There were no real old men there. To his surprise the Lamas considered Colonel Bradford a quite novel sight, for it had been a long time since they had seen anyone who looked as old as he. The Lamas good-naturedly referred to the Colonel as "The Ancient One."

"For the first two weeks after I arrived," said the Colonel, "I was like a fish out of water. I marvelled at everything I saw, and at times could hardly believe what my eyes beheld. I soon felt much better, was sleeping like a top every night, and only used my cane when hiking in the mountains.

"About three months after I arrived I received the biggest surprise of my life. In fact, I was quite startled. It was the day I entered for the first time, a large, well-ordered room which was used as a kind of library for ancient manuscripts. At one end of the room was a full-length mirror. It had been over two years since I had last seen my reflection, so with great curiosity I stepped in front of the glass.

"I stared in amazement, so changed was my appearance. It seemed that I had dropped 15 years from my age. It was my first intimation that I was growing younger; but from then on I changed so rapidly that it was apparent to all who knew me.

Soon the honorary title of "The Ancient One" was heard no more."

A knock at the door interrupted the Colonel. I opened it to admit a couple of friends from out of town who had picked this most inauspicious time to spend a sociable evening with me. I hid my disappointment and chagrin as best I could and introduced them to Colonel Bradford. We all chatted together for a short time, and then the Colonel said, as he arose:

"I am sorry that I must leave so early, but I have an appointment with an old friend who is leaving the city tonight. I hope I shall see you all again shortly."

At the door he turned to me and said, softly, "Could you have lunch with me tomorrow? I promise, if you can do so, you shall hear all about 'The Fountain of Youth.'"

We agreed as to the time and place and the Colonel departed. As I returned to the living room, one of my friends remarked,

"That is certainly a most interesting man, but he looks awfully young to be retired from Army service."

"How old do you suppose he is?" I asked.

"Well, he doesn't look forty," answered my friend, "but from the experiences he has had I suppose he must be that old."

"Yes, he's all of that," I replied evasively, and deftly turned the conversation into another channel. I thought it best to arouse no wonderment regarding the Colonel until

I knew what his plans were.

The next day, after having lunch together, we repaired to the Colonel's room in a nearby hotel, and there at last he told me about "The Fountain of Youth."

"The first important thing I was taught after entering the Lamasery," he began, "was this. The body has seven centers which, in English, could be called Vortexes. These are kind of magnetic centers. They revolve at great speed in the healthy body, but when slowed down – well, that is just another name for old age, ill-health, and senility.

"There are two of these Vortexes in the brain; one at the base of the throat; another in the right side of the body opposite the liver; one in the sexual center; and one in each knee.

"These spinning centers of activity extend beyond the flesh in the healthy individual, but in the old, weak, senile person they hardly reach the surface, except in the knees. The quickest way to regain health, youth, and vitality is to start these magnetic centers spinning again.

"There are but five practices that will do this. Any one of them, especially the first, will be helpful, but all five are usually required to get glowing results. These five exercises are really not exercises at all, in the physical culture sense. The Lamas think of them as 'Rites,' and so instead of calling them exercises or practices, we too, shall call them Rites."

THERE ARE SEVEN PSYCHIC VORTEXES IN THE PHYSICAL BODY

- **Vortex "A"** is located deep within the forehead
- **Vortex "B"** is in the posterior part of the brain
- **Vortex "C"** located in throat at the base of the neck
- **Vortex "D"** located in the right side of the body (waist line)
- **Vortex "E"** is in the reproductive anatomy or organs
- **Vortexes "F"** and "**G**" located one in either knee.

These Psychic Vortexes revolve at great speed. When all are revolving at the same speed the body is in good health.

When one or more of them slow down, old age, loss of power, or senility begin to set in almost immediately.

You can download this poster for free on *T5T.com* website.

RITE
NUMBER ONE

" The first Rite," continued the Colonel "is a simple one. It is for the express purpose of speeding up the Vortexes. When we were children we used it in our play. It is this: Stand erect with arms outstretched, horizontal with the shoulders. Now spin around until you become slightly dizzy. There is only one caution: you must turn from left to right. In other words, if you were to place a clock or watch on the floor face up, you would turn in the same way the hands are moving.

"At first the average adult will only be able to "spin around" about a half-dozen times until he becomes dizzy enough to want to sit or lie down. That is just what he should do, too. That's what I did. To begin with, practice this Rite only to the point of slight dizziness.[3] As time passes and your Vortexes become more rapid in movement through this and other Rites, you will be able to practice it to a greater extent.

> *(3) If you experience dizziness, don't be disheartened as it usually improves over time. I have seen fit people, and those who practice yoga regularly (including teachers) take around six months to build up to 21 repetitions of the spin because of dizziness. By far, the vast majority of people have no trouble at all unless they try to do too many repetitions, too quickly. It is best to build up repetitions gradually to allow your body's balance systems to adjust to the movement. See tips and natural remedies for dizziness below.*

"When I was in India it amazed me to see the Maulawiyah, or as they are more commonly known, the Whirling Dervishes, almost unceasingly spin around and around in a religious frenzy. Rite Number One recalled to my attention two things in connection with this practice. The first was that these Whirling Dervishes always spun in one direction - from left to right, or clockwise. The second was the virility of the old men; they were strong, hearty, and robust. Far more than most Englishmen are at their age.

"When I spoke to one of the Lamas about this, he informed me that while this whirling movement of the Dervishes did have a very beneficial effect, yet it also had a devastating one. It seems that a long siege of whirling stimulates into great activity Vortexes "A," "B," and "E." These three have a stimulating effect on the other two– "C" and "D." But due to excessive leg action the Vortexes in the knees– "E" and "G" –

are over-stimulated and finally so exhausted that the building up of the Vital Forces along with this tearing down causes the participants to experience a kind of "psychic jag" which they mistake for something very spiritual.

"However," continued the Colonel, "we do not carry the whirling exercise to excess. While the whirling Dervishes may spin around many hundreds of times, we find that greater benefit is obtained by restricting it to about a dozen or so times, or enough so that Rite Number One can stimulate all the Vortexes to action. After several months it can be increased to 20 revolutions. Later to 30, 40, and eventually, after many months, to 50."

The symptoms of dizziness/motion sickness occur because your brain receives conflicting information from your sensory systems. These senses send information to your brain about the position and movement of your body. This includes your eyes, the sensors of the semicircular canals in your inner ears, and the somatosensory receptors in your skin, joints, and muscles. A mismatch in sensory information causes a conflict between what is seen or felt and your previous orientational experience. When this happens, the body responds with the symptoms of dizziness and motion sickness. For this reason, using the correct technique during the spin is crucial.

Try fine-tuning your movement or using one or more of the natural remedies for dizziness outlined below.

IMPROVE YOUR SPIN TECHNIQUE

1. **Slow Down.** Don't try and complete too many rotations too quickly. Allow your body time to get used to the motion.

2. **Do Fewer Repetitions.** Some people take six months or more to build up to the required 21 repetitions.

Dizziness affects people differently regardless of their fitness level. I have taught yoga teachers & long-term yoga practitioners who experienced dizziness in the early stages of learning the Spin. Do only as many repetitions as you can without becoming uncomfortably dizzy. Gradually add repetitions over a period of weeks or even months until you can do the required 21 repetitions easily. Ensure all dizziness has disappeared (to prevent nausea) before moving onto Rite No. 2.

3. **Continue To Build Repetitions Of Rites, 2, 3, 4, and 5** in the recommended manner (3 repetitions in your first week, then add 2 per week until you are doing 21 repetitions in around ten weeks). Gradually increase the number of spins until you catch up with the other Rites.

4. **Fine Tune Your Movement.** Fine-tune your movement so it is smooth from head to toe. Steps that are too large, too small, too bouncy, or steps that start and stop instead of flowing from one to another create a motion of their own and contribute to dizziness. A smooth movement improves aerodynamics and reduces motion.

5. **Flat And Solid Level Surface.** Do not spin on an uneven surface as this increases dizziness, and you will find it hard to keep your balance. Doing the Rites outside in nature is wonderful, but choose your surface carefully. Soft sand isn't suitable if you are going to try it on a beach.

6. **Important - Keep Your Spin Movement Contained Within A Small, Obstacle Free Area.** If you wander across the floor, slow down and adjust your movement. Bring your legs to hip-width apart and take small (not

jerky) flowing steps. If you come into contact with an obstacle, avoid looking at it until you have stopped spinning and your dizziness has abated. Otherwise, you will feel very dizzy and may stagger or fall. In T5T, we carry out three special Energy Breaths after spinning. We place our hands on our hips and keep our eyes closed. You could try taking three deep, slow breaths instead.

7. **Remember to Breathe!** People often hold their breath while spinning, which reduces the oxygen supply to the brain and increases the likelihood of dizziness. Get into a habit of taking a breath before you begin spinning and constantly remind yourself to breathe normally while performing the Spin.

ALTERNATIVE TO THE SPIN

In the rare likelihood that dizziness becomes a problem for you – try this alternative.

Simply swing your arms at shoulder height around to the opposite shoulder, and repeat to the other side. Your head and upper body twist around to one side and then the other. Your feet remain stationary, but remember to lift the opposite heel to the direction you are turning to avoid straining your lower back.

NATURAL REMEDIES FOR DIZZINESS

- **Lemon and Ginger.** Before you spin, drink a small glass of hot or cold water with some freshly squeezed lemon juice and a small slice of fresh ginger. This can help with dizziness and nausea. **Peppermint or chamomile tea** is also good for soothing the stomach.

- **Apple cider vinegar and honey** drunk twice daily are also effective against dizziness.
- **Take a supplement of Ginkgo Biloba or feverfew.** These herbal remedies help with dizziness. Check with your doctor first if you are taking any medication.
- **Fresh Air.** Spin in an area with plenty of fresh air – avoid stuffy rooms.
- **Special Acupressure Point.** Pressing on the "Nei-Guan" acupressure point helps reduce dizziness and nausea – often within a few minutes. After spinning, circle your fingers and thumb around your wrist approximately three fingers-width below the wrist folding line – with your thumb in the depression between the two flexor tendons. When you find a slightly tender spot, press your fingers and thumbs in towards each other. You can also buy inexpensive motion sickness or anti-nausea bracelets with built-in buttons that press on this point.
- **Avoid** eating a heavy meal or drinking alcoholic beverages before spinning.
- **Limit** your intake of salt or caffeine. These substances may impair the circulation of your blood, as will smoking.
- **Learn to manage stress.** Doing the Five Rites will help greatly with this.

SOME EXERCISES YOU CAN DO TO HELP PREVENT DIZZINESS

These exercises help strengthen your body's balance systems and reduce motion sickness.

- Lookup, and then look down. Repeat this movement several times while increasing the speed from slow to rapid. Now look from left to right, going from slow to fast as before. Repeat these eye movements several times a day.
- In a sitting or standing position, toss a tennis ball from hand to hand. Follow the arc of the ball with your eyes.
- Place a stable chair next to a wall so you can reach out and touch it if needed. Sit on the chair with your feet flat on the floor. Focus your eyes on a target three to six meters (10 to 20 feet) away while you stand up slowly and then sit down again with your eyes open. Repeat this several times, and then try the same exercise with your eyes closed (lightly touching the wall for security if and when needed.)
- Clear a path next to a wall or behind a sofa. Walk backward and forwards alongside the wall or sofa several times. Then, by holding onto the wall or the couch, close your eyes and repeat the same exercise several times.

7

RITE
NUMBER TWO

First Position of Rite No. 2

To perform this Rite lie full length on rug or bed. Place the hands flat down alongside the hips. Fingers should be kept close together with the finger-tips of each hand turned slightly toward one another.

Second Position of Rite No. 2

Raise the feet until the legs are straight up. If possible, let the feet extend back a bit over the body toward the head, but do not let the knees bend. Hold this position for a moment or two and then slowly lower the feet to the floor, and for the next several moments allow all of the muscles in the entire body to relax completely. Then perform the Rite all over again.

While the feet and legs are being raised it is a good idea also to raise the head, then while the feet and legs are being lowered to the floor lower the head at the same time.

By raising the head at the same time the legs and feet are raised, all of the Vortexes in the body are increased in their speed or action, but especially the slow ones.

RITE NO 2 – THE LEG RAISE

"Like Rite Number One," continued the Colonel, "this second one is for further stimulating to action the Seven Vortexes. It is even simpler than the first one. In Rite Number Two, one first lies flat on his back on the floor or on the bed.[4] If practiced on the floor, one should use a rug or blanket under him, folded several times in order that the body will not come into contact with the cold floor.

> (4)　*Avoid practicing the Leg Raise on your bed unless your bed is very firm. Sagging in the mattress caused by your body weight changes the natural and optimal S-shape of your spine, creating additional strain on the supporting muscles that wrap around your spine, and may lead to injury.*

The Lamas have what in English might be called a 'prayer rug.' It is about two feet wide and fully six feet long. It is fairly thick and is made from wool and a kind of vegetable fibre. It is solely for the purpose of insulation, and so has no other value. Nevertheless, to the Lamas everything is of a religious nature, hence their name for these mats – 'prayer rugs.'

"As I said, one should lie full length on his 'prayer rug' or bed. Then place the hands flat down alongside the hips. The fingers should be kept close together with the fingertips of each hand turned slightly toward one another. The feet are then raised until the legs are straight up. If possible, let the feet extend back a bit over the body, toward the head; but do not let the knees bend.[5] Then, slowly lower the feet to the floor and for a moment allow all muscles to relax. Then perform this Rite all over again.

(5) *Avoid bringing your legs back over the stomach, as illustrated above, as it takes the spine out of its natural 'neutral' position. Neutral spine is a term used to describe the natural S-shape of the spine when its natural curves are maintained. The muscles closest to the spine (the core muscles) are more effective at stabilizing and protecting the spine (like guide wires on a tent) when the spine is in neutral.*

When you bring your legs back over your stomach, as illustrated above, your tailbone lifts, and the curve of your lower back is flattened to the floor. Instead – only raise your legs to a point where your knee bones are aligned over your hip bones (joint over joint), and the natural curve of your lower back remains intact. It makes no difference to the benefits of the Rites if you don't bring your legs back over your stomach, but the most optimal way you can do the leg raise is with your core muscles activated to protect your spine.

In T5T, we teach you how to identify your core muscles as opposed to the more external muscles of the trunk and how to establish and maintain neutral spine and neutral pelvis. If you don't know how to do this correctly, consider attending a few Pilates classes, or learn from one of the T5T resources listed at the back of the book. Instead of being like a soft-centered chocolate, with toned muscles on the outside and weak muscles on the inside (around the spine)–core stability strengthens you from the inside out to protect and stabilize your spine.

As we get older, it is considered a 'natural part of life' that we will experience varying degrees of degeneration of the spine, discs, and joints of the body. This includes calcification, bone spurs, arthritis, wearing down of the discs, plus general wear and tear. My osteopath calls this 'rust.' Since we don't have X-ray vision, we have little to no awareness of what is occurring inside our bodies until we experience aches, pains, and stiffness, etc.

So if you do carry out this movement as described by Kelder, please take note of any warnings from your body that you may be overexerting yourself. Stick with Colonel Bradford's recommendations of building repetitions gradually (three repetitions per day in your first week, then add two additional repetitions per day per week until you are up to the required 21 repetitions in around ten weeks).

If you have suffered from back or neck pain in the past, are unfit or overweight, I recommend you bend your knees in the beginning and gradually straighten them over time. If you experience any strain or discomfort in your lower back or neck, it should be viewed as a message from your body to stop, review, and adjust. It is easy to swap to the 10-step, T5T method so you can achieve this posture with ease.

"One of the Lamas told me that when he first attempted to practice this simple Rite he was so old, weak, and decrepit that he couldn't possibly lift up both legs. Therefore he started out by lifting the thighs until the knees were straight up, letting the feet hang down. Little by little, however, he was able to straighten out his legs until eventually he could raise them straight with perfect ease.

"I marveled at this particular Lama," said the Colonel, "when he told me this. He was then a perfect picture of health and youth, although I knew he was many years older than he looked.

For the sheer joy of exerting himself, he used to carry up a pack of vegetables weighing fully a hundred pounds on his back, from the garden to the Lamasery, several hundred feet above. He took his time but never stopped once on the way up, and when he would arrive he didn't seem to be experiencing the slightest bit of fatigue. I marveled greatly at this, for the first time I started up with him, and I was carrying no load, I had to stop at least a dozen times. Later I was able to do it easily without my cane and with never a stop."

COLONEL BRADFORD & THE T5T VERSION

"To start with," said he, "I would suggest you practice each Rite three times a day for the first week. Then increase them by two a day each week until you are doing 21 a day, which will be at the beginning of the 10th week."

~ **Colonel Bradford** in *The Eye of Revelation*.

T5T follows these instructions. Where T5T differs is that it offers the additional benefit of a step-by-step core strength development method that teaches you how to strengthen the deepest muscles of the body closest to the spine. These muscles, when correctly activated, wrap around and protect the spine just like a natural weight-belt or a girdle.

- In T5T, **there are ten variations to this leg raise (a new one every week for ten weeks)**, starting with a single leg movement, keeping the knee bent until your knee bone is aligned over your hip bone before straightening your leg.

- **Each week a new variation is added** to develop the strength of the core muscles progressively. Just like learning to lift weights, you begin with low weights (in this case, the natural weight of your legs), gradually increasing the weight (changing the way you do the movement), and the number of repetitions.

- It is essential to learn how to **correctly identify and activate your core muscles** because it is easy to use the stronger, more external muscles instead - leaving the inner muscles undeveloped. Strong core muscles protect your lower back and neck and offer a major bonus for every movement you make in your normal life – not just during your Five Tibetan Rites practice.

6

RITE NUMBER THREE

First Position of Rite No. 3

This Rite – No 3 – should always follow Rite No 2. The first position of this Rite is to kneel on a rug or mat with hands at sides, palms flat against the side of the legs. Then lean forward as far as possible,[6] bending at the waist, with head well forward – chin on chest.

(6) *Kelder's drawing doesn't illustrate the "bending at the waist" that he describes in his text. So what should you do? In the T5T method, we generally avoid bending at the waist so we can align our hip bones over our knee bones and use this strong, stable foundation to lengthen the spine*

before arching backward. We avoid compression of the vertebrae and discs by keeping the spine 'long and strong' throughout the movement.

Overextending the lower back and neck can lead to strain or injury in some people. Once you have learned how to do this properly, you can try the bending forwards first before arching backward.

Make certain you remember to keep your spine 'long and strong' as you arch backward and on the way back to the kneeling position.

In T5T, we teach students how to achieve a 'long and strong' spine by learning how to do the posture with their stomachs pressed gently against a wall. The contact with the wall enables them to feel the upwards and backward arching movement, followed by the forwards and downwards movement as the body returns to the starting position. If students lengthen their spines too far, their ribs will puff out; their lower backs will hollow, and they will be pushed away from the wall. In this way, students learn how to correctly lengthen the spine to a point before the ribs puff out. The natural curves of the spine remain intact if done correctly. Once learned, students are able to perform the posture away from the wall.

Second Position of Rite No. 3

The second position of this Rite is to lean backward as far as possible.[7] Cause the head to move still further backward. The toes will prevent you from falling over backward.

(7) *We recommend you do not follow the instructions by Kelder to "lean back as far as possible." The problems associated with this are that beginners immediately try to achieve this by leaning back on their thighs instead. Instead of aligning*

their thighs over their knee bones, they are angled away from the joint. This strains the knee and hip joints and can also strain the thigh and groin muscles, particularly as repetitions increase.

"Leaning as far back as possible" creates an immense load on the muscles of the lower back to perform the movement and counter the effects of gravity at the same time. It is best to keep your spine aligned as if you were standing upright. Lift your breast bone upwards without puffing out your ribs (to lengthen your spine) before arching backward. Keep your hip bones aligned over your knee bones.

Performing the movement in this manner looks less strenuous than the original, but this is deceptive. Apart from reducing the risk of injury, you get a strong stretch in the front of the chest and between the shoulder blades, particularly if you squeeze your shoulder blades together at the back to increase the stretch. The chest and shoulder blades are two areas of the body that become stiff due to our daily forward actions. We have very few natural movements in our daily lives that cause us to lean backward, and stiffness and loss of mobility occur where we overuse some muscles and underuse others. It is very satisfying to stretch and relieve tension in these areas when doing the backbend, but remember to keep the spine long and strong to avoid compression.

The hands are always kept against the side of the legs. Next come to an erect (kneeling) position, relax as much as possible for a moment, and perform Rite all over again.

RITE NO 3 – THE KNEELING BACKBEND

"The third Rite should be practiced immediately after practicing Rite Number Two. It, too, is a very simple one. All one needs to do is to kneel on his 'prayer rug,' place his hands on his thighs, and lean forward as far as possible with the head inclined so that the chin rests on the chest. Now lean backward as far as possible; at the same time the head should be lifted and thrown back as far as it will go.[8] Then bring the head up along with the body. Lean forward again and start the rite all over. This Rite is very effective in speeding up Vortexes 'E,' 'D,' and 'C'; especially 'E.'

(8)   *For the same reasons as mentioned in No. 7 above, we do not recommend that you "throw the head back as far as it will go," as this compresses the vertebrae and discs in your neck. It is best to keep your neck long and strong, with your core muscles activated to protect your lower back.*

No human skeleton is identical: people's bones vary in size, orientation, and proportion, and for some people bending the neck back too far can occlude (kink) the vertebral artery, reducing oxygen supply to the brain. If you get dizzy or feel a bit faint – avoid dropping your head back so far and keep your neck long and strong.

"I have seen more than 200 Lamas perform this Rite together. In order to turn their attention within, they closed their eyes. In this way they would not become confused by what others were doing and thus have their attention diverted.

"The Lamas, millenniums ago, discovered that all good things come from within. They discovered that <u>every worthwhile thing has its origin within the individual</u>. This is something that the Occidental has never been able to understand and comprehend. He thinks, as I did, that all worthwhile things must come from the outside world.

"The Lamas, especially those at this particular Lamasery, are performing a great work for the world. It is performed, however, on the astral plane. This plane, from which they assist mankind in all quarters of the globe, is high enough above the vibrations of the world to be a powerful focal point where much can be accomplished with little loss of effort."

"Someday the world will awaken in amazement to what the unseen forces – the Forces of Good – have been doing for the masses. We who take ourselves in hand and make new creatures of ourselves in every imaginable way, each is doing a marvelous work for mankind everywhere. Already the efforts of these advanced individuals are being welded together into One Irresistible Power. It is only through individuals like the Lamas, and you and me, that the world can possibly be helped.

"Most of mankind, and that includes those in the most enlightened countries, like America, Canada and England, is still in the darkest of the Dark Ages. However, they are being prepared for better and more glorious things, and as fast as they can be initiated into the higher life, just that fast will the world be made a better place in which to live."

RITE
NUMBER FOUR

First Position of Rite No. 4

Sit erect on rug or carpet with feet stretched out in front. The legs must be perfectly straight – back of knees must be well down or close to the rug. Place the hands flat on the rug, fingers together, and the hands pointing outward slightly. Chin should be on chest – head forward.

Second Position of Rite No. 4

Now gently raise the body, at the same time bend the knees so that the legs from the knees down are practically straight up and down. The arms, too, will also be vertical while the body from shoulders to knees will be horizontal.

As the body is raised upward allow the head gently to fall backward so that the head hangs backward as far as possible when the body is fully horizontal.[9] Hold this position for a few moments, return to first position and RELAX for a few minutes before performing the Rite again.

(9)   *Avoid letting the "head hang backward as far as possible" to prevent compression of the cervical spine and vertebral artery. Keep the neck long and strong.*

RITE NO 4 – THE TABLETOP

"Now for Rite Number Four," said the Colonel. "The first time I tried this it seemed very difficult, but after a while it was as simple to do as any of the others.[10]

(10) *If you find this posture difficult, you can learn from any of the T5T resources listed at the back of this book, where this movement is broken down into three 'learning steps.' After learning the first step, you simply move onto the next, and before you know it, you will find yourself in the tabletop position, wondering how you got there.*

If you are overweight or have weak arm or leg muscles, you can carry out T5T's steps 1 or 2 until your strength builds up sufficiently to carry out the full tabletop position.

You can also prop your hands on yoga blocks or folded
towels (nothing slippery or uneven like cushions). Another
tip is to try moving your hands backward and forwards in
the starting position until you find the most comfortable
position where your center of gravity in the tabletop
position is maintained – not too much weight on the
shoulders or on the legs. Flatten all ten toes to the floor
and align your knees over your ankles.

"Sit on the 'prayer rug' with the feet stretched out in front.
Then place the hands alongside the body. Now raise the body
and bend the knees so that the legs, from the knees down, are
practically straight up and down. The arms, too, will be straight
up and down, while the body, from the shoulders to the knees,
will be horizontal. Before pushing the body to a horizontal
position, the chin should be well down on the chest. Then, as
the body is raised, the head should be allowed to drop gently
backward as far as it will go. Next, return to a sitting position
and relax for a moment before repeating the procedure. When
the body is pressed up to the complete horizontal position,
tense every muscle in the body. This will have a tendency to
stimulate Vortexes 'F,' 'G,' 'E,' 'D' and C.'

"After leaving the Lamasery," continued Colonel Bradford,
"I went to a number of the larger cities in India, and as an
experiment conducted classes for both English people and
natives. I found that the older members of either felt that unless
they could perform a Rite perfectly, right from the beginning,
they believed no good could come from it. I had considerable
difficulty in convincing them that they were wrong. But after a
good deal of persuasion I was able to get them to do their best,
and the results were more than gratifying.

"I remember in one city I had quite a number of old people
in one of my classes. With this particular Rite   Number Four

– they could just barely get their bodies off the floor; they couldn't get it anywhere near a horizontal position. In the same class were several much younger persons who had no difficulty in performing the Rite perfectly from the very start. This so discouraged the older people that I had to ask the younger ones to refrain from practicing it before their older classmates.

I explained that I could not do it at first, either; that I couldn't do a bit better than any of them; but that I could perform the Rite 50 times in succession now without feeling the slightest strain on nerves or muscles; and in order to convince them, I did it right before their eyes. From then on, the class broke all records for results accomplished."

RITE
NUMBER FIVE

10

First Position of Rite No. 5

The First position of the Rite is to place the hands on the floor about two feet apart. The legs are stretched out to the rear with the feet also about two feet apart. Allow the body to "sag" downward from shoulders to toes. Hold the head as far back as is comfortable. The arms are kept perfectly straight at all times in Rite No. 5

Second Position of Rite No. 5

The Second position is attained by pushing the body, especially the hips, upward as far as possible. The hands are kept flat on the floor at all times. Hold this position for a brief moment and return to First position. After a moment of "hanging in suspension" perform the Rite over again.

RITE NO 5– THE PENDULUM

"The best way[11] to perform this Rite is to place the hands on the floor about two feet apart. Then, with the legs stretched out to the rear with the feet also about two feet apart, push the body, and especially the hips, up as far as possible, rising on the toes and hands. At the same time the head should be brought so far down that the chin comes up against the chest.

> *(11) Actually, we have not found this the easiest way to begin the movement. It requires a lot more physical strength than most beginners are capable of. In T5T, we begin this movement in the upside-down V position, which makes it easier to perform. Like Rite No. 4 above, we break this movement down into three 'learning steps' or easy-to-achieve components, so the final posture is achieved with confidence and ease.*

"Next, allow the body to come slowly down to a 'sagging' position.[12] Bring the head up, causing it to be drawn as far back as possible.

> *(12) Avoid 'sagging' in the lower back as this causes compression. Firm your buttocks and activate your core muscles throughout the movement. If you don't know how to identify and activate the correct core muscles, consider a few Pilates classes or follow the instructions in one of the T5T resources at the back of the book.*

> **Note**: *There is a real tendency to use the momentum of this movement by swinging up and down between the upside-down V position and the plank position. Be very careful to avoid dropping your pelvis too rapidly and too low as you come down from the upside-down V position into the plank-like position. Keep your movement controlled and your technique correct. Keep your core muscles activated and your buttocks firmed (not squeezed tight) to protect your spine.*

"After a few weeks, that is after you become quite proficient in this movement, let the body drop from its highest position to a point almost but not quite touching the floor. The muscles should be tensed for a moment when the body is at the highest point, and again at the lowest point.

"Everywhere I go," went on the Colonel, "folks, at first, call these Rites physical culture exercises. I would like to make it clearly understood that these are not physical culture exercises at all. They are only performed a few times a day; so few times that they could not possibly be of any value as physical culture movements. What the Rites actually do is this: They start the seven Vortexes spinning at a normal rate of speed; at the speed which is normal for, say, a young, robust, strong, virile man of twenty-five years of age.

"Now in such a person the Vortexes are all spinning normally at the same rate of speed. On the other hand, if you could view the seven Vortexes of the average middle-aged man – weak, unhealthy, and semi-virile, as he is – you would notice at once that some of the Vortexes had greatly slowed down in their spinning movement; and worse still, all were spinning at a different rate of speed – none of them working together in harmony. The slower ones allowed that part of the body which they govern to degenerate, deteriorate, and become diseased.

"The only INNER difference between youth and senility is simply the difference in the rate of speed at which the Vortexes are spinning. Normalize the different speeds, and the old man becomes a new man again."

THE FIVE RITES
– ON ONE PAGE

You can download this free poster on the *T5T.com* website.

Consider this: When you have built up to 21 repetitions of each movement (five postures performed 21 times each), you will be doing 105 repetitions per day. Over a year (365 days), that is 38,325 repetitions. As you can imagine, it is vital to have your alignment and technique correct from the word go.

11

FURTHER INFORMATION

W hen the Colonel had finished his description of the Five Rites I stopped him a moment.

"Let me ask you some questions now."

"Very well," he replied. "That is just what I want you to do."

"I feel that from your description I understand the Rites quite well," I began, "but when and how often are they to be employed?"

"They can be used either night and morning," answered the Colonel, "in the morning only, or just at night, if it is more convenient. I use them both morning and night, but I would not advise so much stimulation for the beginner until he has practiced them for a number of months. At the start he could use them the full number of times in the morning, and then in the evening he could gradually build up until finally he is doing the same amount of practice as in the morning."

"Just how many times a day should a person use these Rites?" was my next question.

"To start with," said he, "I would suggest you practice each Rite three times a day for the first week. Then increase them by two a day each week until you are doing 21 a day; which will be at the beginning of the 10th week.[13]

(13) Everyone wants to reach the goal of 21 repetitions, and it is worth reminding yourself to enjoy the journey as well as the destination.

People who practice yoga regularly or keep themselves fit may want to progress at a much faster rate than Colonel Bradford recommends. This is understandable, but please remember that these exercises are designed to have a stimulating effect on the energy systems of your body. If, after having performed the Rites, you find it difficult to relax or remain focused; are moodier than usual; have difficulty sleeping, or feel you are "not in" your body – then reduce repetitions and build up more gradually.

DETOX EFFECTS

Due to the increased elimination of impurities and wastes and elevated oxygen levels in your body, you may experience some minor detox effects. Some people have strong changes, and others have none at all. If you do experience any of the following symptoms, they usually settle down within one to two weeks.

A metallic taste in the mouth.

Achy joints for a day or so.

Darker, stronger-smelling urine.

Diarrhoea or a strong bowel movement.

Initial constipation.

Slight nausea.

Initial fatigue as body balances itself.

Cold or flu-like symptoms that last a day.

A runny nose as sinuses clear.

A tic or involuntary muscle movement over one eye. A mild rash or pimples.

Moodiness, either a bit snappy or teary.

"If you cannot practice Rite Number One, the whirling one, the same number of times as the others, then do it only as many times as you can without getting too dizzy. The time will soon come, however, when you can practice it the full number of 21 times.

"If, for any reason, one or more of the Rites cannot be used at all, do not be discouraged; use the ones you can. Results will be a little slower, but that will be the only handicap.

"If one has been recently operated on for, say, appendicitis, or is afflicted with hernia, he should be very cautious in practicing Rites Numbers Two, Three, and Five. If one is very heavy, he should be cautious in the use of Number Five until his weight has been greatly reduced.

"All five of the Rites are of importance. Even though he may not be able to perform them the prescribed number of times the individual may rest assured that just a few times each day will be of benefit.

"I knew of one man who required more than a year before he could do it that many times. But he performed the other four without difficulty, gradually increasing the number until he was doing the full 21 on all four. He got very splendid results.

"Under certain conditions," added the Colonel, "there are some who find it difficult to perform Rite Number One at all, to begin with. But after having done the other four for about six months they are amazed at how easy it is to do Number One. Likewise with the other Rites. If for any reason one or more of them cannot be used, do not be discouraged; use what you can. Results, in that case, will be a little slower, but that is the only handicap.

"If one has been recently operated on for, say, appendicitis, or is afflicted with hernia, he should be very cautious in practicing Rites Number Two and Five. If one is very heavy, he should be cautious in the use of Number Five until his weight has been greatly reduced.

"All five of the Rites are of importance. Even though he may not be able to perform them the prescribed number of times, the individual may rest assured that just a few times each day will be of benefit.

"If, at the end of the fourth week, one finds that he cannot perform every one of the Rites the required number of times, he should note carefully the ones which he is forced to slight. Then, if he is performing the Five Rites in the morning, he should try to make up the deficiency in the evening. Or if he is performing the Rites in the evening, he should endeavor to find time in the morning to catch up.

In either event he should not neglect the other Rites, and *above all he should never strain himself.* If he goes about performing the Rites in an easy, interesting manner it will not be long before he finds everything working out satisfactorily, and that he is doing the Rites the required 21 times a day.

"Some people, acting on their own initiative, invent little aids for their practices. An old fellow in India found it impossible for him to perform Rite Number Four properly even once. He wouldn't be satisfied with just getting his body off the floor; he was determined that it should reach a horizontal position as the Rite prescribed. So he got a box about ten inches high and two and a half feet long. Upon this he put some bedding folded to the right size, and across this padded box he lay flat on his back. Then, with his feet on the floor at one end and his hands on the floor at the other he found it quite simple to raise his body to a horizontal position.

"Now while this little 'stunt' may not in itself have helped the old gentleman in performing the Rite the full 21 times, still the psychological effect of being able to raise his body as high as the much stronger men was undoubtedly quite stimulating and may have been quite beneficial. I do not particularly recommend this old man's aid, although it may help those who think it impossible to make progress in any other way; but if you have an inventive mind you will think of ways and means to help you in performing the more difficult Rites.

"These Rites are so powerful that if one were left out entirely while the other four were practiced regularly the full number of times, only the finest kind of results would be experienced. The First Rite alone will do wonders as evidenced by the Whirling Dervishes of whom we spoke. Had they spun around only a limited number of times, they would have found themselves greatly benefited, although they may not have attributed their improved condition to the whirling. The fact that they whirled from left to right and that the old men were virile and strong is ample proof that just this one Rite will have powerful effects.

"So if anyone finds that they simply cannot perform all five of these Rites, or that they cannot perform them all the full number of times, they may know that good results may still be experienced."

"Does anything else go with these Five Rites?" I asked.

"There is one more thing - just a suggestion. Take either a tepid bath or a cool, but not cold, one after practicing the Rites.

"Going over the body quickly with a wet towel and then with a dry one is probably even better. One thing I must caution you against: you must never take a shower, tub, or wet towel bath which is cold enough to chill you even slightly internally. If you do, you will have undone all the good you have gained from performing the Five Rites."

"This all seems so simple," I ventured, "Do you mean to tell me that this is all that is necessary in the work of restoring the prematurely old to robust health, vigor, and virility?"

"All that is required," answered the Colonel, "is to practice the Five Rites three times a day to begin with, and gradually increase them as I have explained until each is being practiced 21 times each day. That is all; there is nothing more.

"Of course," he continued, "one must practice them every day in order to keep one's robust vitality. You may skip one day a week, but never more than that. The use of the Five Rites is no hardship at all; it requires less than 10 minutes a day to practice them. If necessary one can get up ten minutes earlier or go to bed ten minutes later.

"The Five Rites are for the express purpose of restoring a man to manhood. That is, to make him virile and keep him that way constantly. Whether or not he will make the comeback in youthful appearance, as I have done in so short a time, depends on how he uses his virility.

"Some men do not care whether they look young, or even whether they appear young, just so long as they have all their manly powers. But as for me, I was an old man for so many years that I like the idea of throwing off the years in every way possible."

12

BREATHING

There are **NO** instructions for breathing given when practicing The Five Rites (movements themselves) in either the original 1939 or 1946 versions of "The Eye of Revelation" written by Peter Kelder. It is only in later reprints by other publishers that breathing is mentioned at all! The exception is the *6th Rite,* which is a breathing exercise.

Since correct respiration is such a vital contributor to our overall health, energy, and wellbeing, I have added natural full breathing instruction and exercises to T5T.

Breathing is so significant. It supplies life-giving energy (prana, chi) as well as oxygen to our bodies and removes wastes, and a number of clinical studies have proven that how well you breathe literally dictates your lifespan. Consider this:

"The average person reaches peak respiratory function and lung capacity in their mid-twenties. Then they begin to lose respiratory capacity: between 10% and 27% for every decade of life. Unless you are doing something to maintain or improve your breathing capacity, it will decline, and with it, your general health, your life expectancy, and for that matter, your spirit as well."

References:

1. **The Framingham study** These researchers were able to foretell how long a person was going to live by measuring forced exhalation breathing volume, FEV1, and hypertension. We know that much of hypertension is controlled by the way we breathe. "Long before a person becomes terminally ill, vital capacity can predict life span." William B. Kannel of Boston School of Medicine (1981)

2. **University at Buffalo.** Schunemann HJ, Dorn J, Grant BJB, Winkelstein W, Jr., Trevisan M. Pulmonary Function Is a Long-term Predictor of Mortality in the General Population 29-Year Follow-up of the Buffalo Health Study. Chest 2000;118 (3)656-664.

3. **University of Pavia, Italy,** discovered that slowing the respiratory rate to 6 breaths a minute reduces shortness of breath, improves pulmonary gas exchange and exercise performance in patients with CHF. Practicing slow and deep breathing thus can be beneficial in heart failure or in other diseases. (Source: Lancet. 1998 May 2; 351(9112):1308-11.)

"Did you know that given an optimal diet, the respiratory system should be responsible for eliminating 70% of your metabolic waste? The remainder should be eliminated through defecation 3%, urination 8%, and perspiration 19%. So, if you think that going to the bathroom every day is important, or that working up a good sweat now and then is healthy, think again about the value of full free optimal breathing."

~ **Mike White,** Optimal Breathing

It makes perfect sense to include natural full breathing with the Rites. Breathing in fills your body with life-giving oxygen, and breathing out eliminates toxins and wastes.

In T5T we teach you how to breathe slower, deeper, fuller, and with less tension. Our 'Energy Breathing Technique' is completed three times between each Rite, and we also teach you how to breathe correctly while performing the Rites.

It isn't the purpose of this book to teach you the T5T method, but to provide you with Kelder's own words along with tips and advice on what to do and what to avoid. Kelder did not leave any instructions for breathing, so this is entirely optional - see T5T resources at the back of the book.

THE FIVE ELEMENTS

13

A t the time of the development of the Five Tibetan Rites of Rejuvenation, the ancients believed that their world was composed of Five Elements; water, earth, air, fire, and spirit (energy).

In psychology, the Five Elements are used to personify different human traits, such as the personality type categories of Carl Jung (feeling, sensing, intuiting, and thinking) and those associated with the astrological signs of the zodiac. I experimented with the concept of assigning an element to each of the Rites and found the results to be amazing.

In each case, the physical movement of the Rite was a metaphor for what we were trying to achieve mentally – awareness in a different aspect of life. For example, the Spin takes the element energy, and the vortex that the movements create allows you to replenish your body from the larger energy all around us. The Tabletop takes the element earth, and its movements focus on stability, foundation, and balance, giving us a solid base from which to form new ideas.

In holistic exercise, it can sometimes be hard to marry the physical state with the mental state, and having a metaphor helps people enormously to align the two, and to present a clear picture of what they are working towards.

Having assigned an element and a modern name to each Rite, I then experimented with creating an affirmation that expressed the "energy" of each movement. The result is a method of reinforcing and focusing upon the positive benefits of each Rite physically, mentally, and spiritually. This has a ripple effect on every area of your life.

- **Rite No. I (Energy)**
  – The Spin – "I am full of energy."
- **Rite No. 2 (Air)**
  – The Leg Raise – "My mind is clear and calm."
- **Rite No. 3 (Water)**
  – The Kneeling Backbend – *"I am flexible and receptive."*
- **Rite No. 4 (Earth)**
  – The Tabletop – "I am strong and balanced."
- **Rite No. 5 (Fire)**
  – The Pendulum – "I am positive and motivated."

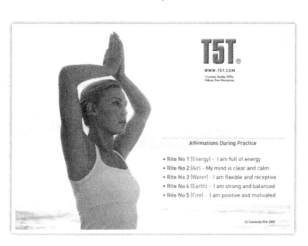

You can download this free Affirmations Poster on the *T5T.com* website.

THE HIMALAYA CLUB – PART TWO

14

I t had been ten weeks since Colonel Bradford's return from India. Much had happened in that time. I had immediately started putting the Five Rites into practice and had been getting results. The Colonel had been busy with some personal business transactions and I saw little of him for a while, but when he once more was at leisure I lost no time telling him of my progress and in enthusiastically expressing my feeling regarding this wonderful new system of regaining vigor, health, power, virility, and vitality.

Ever since the day I was sure that I was well on the way to -ment. The Colonel insisted that the class be limited to not more than 15 members, and I had ten times that number in mind. However, no amount of persuasion and coercion could change his mind.

From the beginning the class was a huge success. We met once a week and my friends all had implicit faith in the Colonel and in the Five Rites. As early as the second week I could see marked improvement in several of them, although, being forbidden to discuss their progress with anyone but the Colonel, I could not verify my impression. However, at the end of a month we held a kind of testimonial meeting. Every man reported improvement. Some told most glowing accounts. A man nearing 75 years of age had made more gains than any of the others.

The weekly meetings of "The Himalaya Club," as we had named it, continued. The tenth week rolled around and practically all of the members were performing all Five Rites 21 times a day. All of them were feeling better and some dropped a number of years from their appearance.

This brought to mind that several of them had asked the Colonel his age but that he had told them he would wait until the end of the tenth week to tell them. This was the evening, but as yet the Colonel had not put in an appearance. Someone suggested that each member write on a slip of paper what age he believed the Colonel to be and then they would compare notes. As the papers were being collected, in walked Colonel Bradford. He was told what had taken place.

"Bring them to me and I shall see how well you have estimated my age. Then I shall tell you what it really is."

The slips all read from 38 to 42. With great amusement the Colonel read them aloud.

"Gentlemen," he said, "I thank you. You are most complimentary. And as you have been honest with me, I shall be equally honest with you. I shall be 73 years of age on my next birthday."

The members stared in consternation and amazement. They found it hard to believe that one so youthful in appearance could have lived so long. Then they wanted to know why, inasmuch as they already felt half their former age, they, too, had not made more progress in youthful appearance.

"In the first place, gentlemen," the Colonel informed them, "you have only been doing this wonderful work for ten weeks. When you have been at it two years you will see a much more pronounced change. Then again, I have not told you all there is to know. I have given you Five Rites which are for the express purpose of restoring one to manly vigor and vitality.

"These Five Rites also make one appear more youthful; but if you really want to look and be young in every respect there is a Sixth Rite that you must practice. I have said nothing about it until now because it would have been useless to you without first having obtained good results from the other five."

The Colonel then informed them that in order to go further with the aid of this Sixth Rite it would be necessary for them to lead a more or less continent life.[14] He suggested that they take a week to think the matter over and decide whether or not they desired to do so for the rest of their lives. Then those who wished to go on would be given Rite Number Six. There were but five who came back the next week, although according to the Colonel this was a better showing than he had experienced with any of his classes in India.

(14) More or less 'continent' means more or less celibate (exercising moderation and self-restraint in appetites and behavior).

When he had first told them about the Sixth Rite, the Colonel had made it clear that the procreative energy would be lifted up, and that this lifting-up process would cause not only the mind to be renewed but the entire body as well; but that it entailed certain restrictions with which the average man did not care to conform. Then he went on with this explanation.

Although there are no instructions provided for women, many thousands of women all over the world have successfully practiced the Rites and obtained the same great benefits as men. It is important to acknowledge that by far, the greatest percentage of practitioners, regardless of their gender, only

*practice the Five Rites. I have found in teaching the many
people I have that the Five Rites alone are sufficient to obtain
the great benefits described in this book.*

"In the average virile man," said the Colonel, "the life forces
course downward, but in order to become a Superman they
must be turned upward. This we call 'The Newer Use of the
Reproductive Energy.' Turning these powerful forces upward
is a very simple matter, yet man has attempted it in many
ways for centuries and in almost every instance has failed.
Whole religious orders in the Occidental World have tried this
very thing, but they, too, have failed because they have tried
to master the procreative energy by suppressing it. There is
only one way to master this powerful urge, and that is not
by dissipating or suppressing it but by TRANSMUTING it -
transmuting it and at the same time lifting it upward. In this
way you really and truly have discovered not only the 'Elixir
of Life,' as the ancients called it, but you have put it to use as
well, which is something the ancients were seldom able to do.

"Now this Rite Number Six is the simplest thing in the
world to perform. It should only be practiced when one has
an excess of procreative energy; when there is a definite
desire for expression. It can be done so easily that it can be
performed anywhere at any time. When one feels the powerful
reproductive urge, here is all that is necessary:

"Stand erect and then let all the air out of the lungs, as one
bends over and places his hands on his knees. Force out the last
trace of air. Then, with empty lungs, stand erect, place hands
on hips, and push down on them. This has a tendency to push
up the shoulders. While doing this, pull in the abdomen just as
far as possible, which raises the chest. Now hold this position
as long as you can. Then when you are forced to take air into

the empty lungs, let the air flow in through the nose. Exhale it through the mouth as you relax the arms and let them hang naturally at your sides. Then take several deep breaths through the mouth or nose and allow them to quickly escape through either the mouth or the nose. This constitutes one complete performance of Rite Number Six. About three are required to subdue the most powerful urge and to turn the powerful procreative or reproductive forces upward.

Interestingly, the Sixth Rite is similar to a yoga practice known as 'Uddiyana Bandha,' which means 'flying upward energy lock.' It is one of three bandhas (energy locks or valves) that are practiced together or individually at specific times during yoga postures, breathing, visualization, meditation, and other yogic practices. They direct energy (prana) throughout the body to release blockages and nourish corresponding areas. They bind or 'lock' the prana to prevent it from dissipating from the body. Bandhas, when released, allows the flow of kundalini energy up the central energy canal in the spinal column, which connects the base chakra to the crown chakra.

"The only difference there is between the average virile man and the Superman is that the average lets the procreative urge flow downward while the Super-man turns the procreative urge upward and reproduces within himself a NEW MAN - a strong, powerful, magnetic man who is constantly growing younger, day by day, moment by moment. This is the true SUPER-MAN, who creates within himself the true 'ELIXIR OF LIFE.' Now you understand why it was unnecessary for me to have left my native England to find the 'Fountain of Youth' – it was within me all the time. Now you can see that when I wrote my friend here some time ago that I had found 'The Fountain of Youth' and was bringing it back with me, I meant just that. The Five Rites and the 'Fountain' are one.

"When I remember Ponce de Leon and his futile search for the 'Fountain' I think of how simple it would have been for him to stay at home and simply use it; but he, like myself, believed it was anywhere in the world except at home - within one's self.

"Please understand that in order to perform Rite Number Six it is absolutely necessary that a man have full masculine virility. He couldn't possibly raise up and transmute procreative energy if there were little or none to transmute. It is absolutely impossible for an impotent man or the one with little virility to perform this Rite. He shouldn't even attempt it, because it would only lead to discouragement, which might do him great harm. Instead he should first practice the other Five Rites until he has full masculine power, and this regardless of how young or how old he may be. Then when the first "full bloom of youth" is experienced within him, he may, then go on to the business of being a SUPER-MAN.

"The man of the world is interested only in the material things of the world, and for that reason should practice only the first five Rites until he feels the urge or desire within to become the SUPER-MAN. Then he should decide definitely; for a clean-cut start and a new life are absolutely necessary to those who lead the SUPER-LIFE. They are the ones who become MYSTICS, OCCULTISTS, and ADEPTS. They it is who truly see with THE EYE OF REVELATION.

"Again I say, let no man concern himself with the upturning of the sex currents until he is thoroughly satisfied in his own mind and heart that he truly desires to lead the life of the MYSTIC; then let him make the step forward, and success will crown his every effort.

RITE
NUMBER SIX

15

From my experience, people who are interested in practicing the Sixth Rite generally fall into two camps. The first will try it and see what happens. The second will carry out further research, such as reading tantric texts or obtaining instruction from recognized tantric teachers.

"The tantric practitioner seeks to use the prana (divine power) that flows through the universe (including one's own body) to attain purposeful goals. These goals may be spiritual, material, or both. Most practitioners of tantra consider mystical experience imperative. Some versions of Tantra require the guidance of a guru."… Dr. Peter Baofu

In the process of working with energy, the tantric practitioner has various tools at hand: Yoga, visualizations, yantras, mantras, mudras, meditation, mind training, identification & internalization of deities, mandalas, feasts, purification achievements, initiations, and more.

"Secrecy protects the tantric practitioner and his practice in several ways. It is said that the power and efficacy of the Vajrayana is dependent upon the devotion and respect of its practitioners. If one were to disclose to non-initiates one's practices and experiences, these would be met with misunderstanding and lack of appreciation, at the very least." Secret of the Vajra World: The Tantric Buddhism of Tibet, Reginald A Ray.

The information about the Sixth Rite, as described in 'The Eye of Revelation,' is very simple and enticing. If you are interested in practicing it, I recommend you undertake further research.

Here are Kelder's instructions on how to do the Sixth Rite:

- Stand erect and then let all the air out of the lungs, as one bends over and places his hands on his knees. Force out the last trace of air.
- Then, with empty lungs, stand erect, place hands on hips, and push down on them. This has a tendency to push up the shoulders.
- While doing this, pull in the abdomen just as far as possible, which raises the chest. Now hold this position as long as you can.
- Then when you are forced to take air into the empty lungs, let the air flow in through the nose.
- Exhale it through the mouth as you relax the arms and let them hang naturally at your sides.
- Then take several deep breaths through the mouth or nose and allow them to quickly escape through either the mouth or the nose.
- This constitutes one complete performance of Rite Number Six. About three are required to subdue the most powerful urge and to turn the powerful procreative or reproductive forces upward.

CHAPTER

LONG-LIVED LAMAS
– PART THREE

16

After the tenth week Colonel Bradford no longer attended each weekly meeting. However, he still kept up his interest in the "Himalaya Club," and from time to time would speak on various subjects which would aid them in their work. Sometimes the members requested him to advise them on some particular subject. For instance, we discussed among ourselves one night the tremendously important part that food played in our lives. How the right food would make us more alive and vigorous while the wrong food would make us sluggish and dull. None of us knew much about the subject, however, so we requested the Colonel to advise us at our next meeting as to the Lamas' policy regarding food.

"In the Himalayan Lamasery where I was a neophyte," said the Colonel, in addressing us the following week, "there are no problems concerning the right foods, nor in getting sufficient food. Each of the Lamas does his share of the work in producing what is needed. Furthermore, all the work is done by the most primitive means. Even the soil is tiled by hand. Of course, the Lamas could use horses and plows if they so desired, but direct contact with the soil, handling it and working with it, seems to add something to man's existence. Personally, it made me feel very strongly that I was a part of the Universal. Not merely working with it or working for it but rather that the Universal and I were one.

"Now it is true that the Lamas are vegetarians, but not strictly so. They do use eggs, butter, and home-made cheese in quantities sufficient to serve certain functions of the brain, body, and nervous system. But aside from this they do not need meat, for all who are strong and virile, and who practice Rite Number Six have no need of meat, fish, or fowl.

"Most of those who join the ranks of the Lamas are men of the world who know little about proper food and diet. Yet they are only in the Grand Retreat in the Himalayas a very short while when they begin to show wonderful signs of physical improvement, due no doubt to the diet in the Lamasery.

"No Lama is choosy about his meals. He can't be because there is little to choose from. A Lama diet consists of good, wholesome food but as a rule it consists of but one article of food at a meal. That in itself is a secret of health. When one eats just one kind of food at a time there can be no clashing of foods in the stomach. Foods clash in the stomach because starches will not mix with proteins. For example, bread, which is starchy, when eaten with meats, eggs, or cheese, which are protein, sets up a reaction in the stomach which often causes not only immediate physical pain, but which contributes as well to a short life and a not particularly merry one.

"Many times in the Lamasery dining hall I have set down to the table along with the Lamas and eaten a meal consisting solely of bread. At other times I have had nothing but fresh vegetables and fresh fruits, while at still another meal I ate nothing but cooked vegetables and cooked fruits. At first I greatly missed the large variety of foods to which I had been accustomed; but after a short while I could eat and enjoy a meal consisting of nothing but dark bread or some one particular fruit. Sometimes it would be a feast of one vegetable.

"The point I wish to bring out to you gentlemen is not that you should resign yourselves to a diet of one kind of food to a meal but that you should keep starches, fruits, and vegetables separate from meats, fish, and fowl at your meals.

"It is permissible to make a meal of just meat. In fact, you could have several kinds of meats to a meal. You can have butter, eggs, and cheese with the meat meal, and dark bread, and, if you wish, coffee, or tea, but you must not end up with anything sweet or starchy. No pies or cakes or puddings.

"Then again, your meal can be strictly starches. Then you can indulge in all the sweet fruits, all the bread, butter, pies, cakes, puddings, and fresh or cooked vegetables you like without feeling any ill effects. But keep these meals separate.

"Butter seems to be a neutral. It can be used with either a starchy meal or with a meat meal. Milk, however, agrees better with starch meals.

"The proper use of eggs was another interesting and beneficial thing that came to my attention while dwelling in the Lamasery. The Lamas would not eat whole eggs unless they were engaged in hard manual labor; then they might eat one, medium-boiled. However, they did indulge to a very great extent in raw egg yolks, discarding the white part. Before I learned better it seemed a waste of perfectly good food to toss the cooked whites of the egg back to the chickens, but now I know that no one should eat the whites of eggs unless he is doing hard manual labor; the egg whites are used only by the muscles.

"Although I had always been aware of the fact that egg yolks were particularly good for one, it wasn't until after I arrived at the Lamasery and had an opportunity to talk with an old Austrian chemist that I learned their true value. Then I was amazed to find out that just common hen eggs contain at least half of the sixteen elements required by the brain, blood, nerves, and tissues. It is true that these elements are only needed in small quantities, but they must be included in the diet if one is to be exceptionally robust and healthy, both mentally and physically.

"There is one thing more of great importance that I learned from the Lamas. They taught me to eat, not slowly for its own sake, but so that I might masticate my food more thoroughly. Their bread is tough and it takes good chewing to reduce it to a liquid before swallowing it, but this I learned to do.

"Everything one eats should be 'digested,' so to speak, in the mouth before allowing it to enter the stomach. Starches, particularly, must be digested in the mouth. Unless they first are thoroughly mixed with saliva they literally are dynamite when they get to the stomach.

"While one can do with little mastication of protein foods, such as meat, fish, and fowl, it is a sensible thing to chew them well anyhow. More nourishment can be obtained from food when it is thoroughly masticated. This necessitates less food, and often the amount can be reduced by one-half.

"Many things which I had casually taken for granted before entering the Lamasery seemed shocking when I left it two years later. One of the first things I noted upon arriving in one of the larger cities in India was the prodigious amount of food consumed by everyone who could afford to do so. I have seen one man eat a quantity of food at a meal sufficient to feed four hard-working Lamas and keep them thriving.

"Variety was another thing which appalled me. Having been in the habit of eating but one or two foods at a meal, it amazed me to count 23 varieties of food one evening on my host's table. No wonder that the English and the Americans have such miserable stomachs and such damnably poor health. They seem to know nothing whatsoever about the kind of food they should eat for health and strength.

"Just the other evening I had dinner with a very learned man. He was an educator and quite an intellectual. He calmly stated, while we waited to be served, that in a few short years the human race could become really worthwhile providing his ideas were thoroughly carried out.

"This man was an excellent dictator type, and I was quite impressed by his knowledge, his original ideas, and his ability to express himself. But when I saw this man's selection of food at the dinner table, my opinion of him changed. It was the most atrocious combination of unnutritive TNT I ever saw. I thought, if I could only give him some simple ideas about food he could become a really worthwhile force for good in the world in a short time.

"The right food, the right combinations of foods, the right amount of food, and the right method of eating food combines to do great things for one. It will enable one to put on weight if he is underweight, and to reduce if he is overweight. Keep in mind these five things:

"Never eat starch and meat at the same meal; although if you are strong and healthy it need not cause you too much concern now.

If coffee bothers you, drink it black, using no milk or cream.
If it bothers you then, discontinue its use.

Chew your food to a liquid and cut down on the amount as much as possible.

By all means and before all else eat raw egg yolks once a day, every day. Take them at meal times but not with after.

Reduce the varieties of food to a minimum. If one is really hungry before he starts eating, the tendency to desire many different foods is lost in hunger."

"It is a very simple matter," continued Colonel Bradford, "to live simply in this highly complex world. Let the world be complex but let your diet, and all matters pertaining to your mental and physical wellbeing be simple. One can do this and still lead a very active life in the modern world. Not all Lamas in India live constantly in Lamaseries. Many of them are found in the cities where they are engaged in professions, or are at the head of great business institutions. These men, like their brother Lamas in secluded Lamaseries, live to amazing ages – amazing to the Western World, but quite a commonplace thing in the East. Just how old these Lamas are I do not know from first-hand experience, but I have been reliably informed that some of them remain in the flesh in a hale and hearty condition five to ten times longer than do most people of the Western World."

Around the same time as 'The Eye of Revelation,' Dr. William Howard Hay published (1933) a ground-breaking book, 'A New Health Era,' in which he maintains that all disease is caused by acid accumulation in the body. The Hay Diet, also known as 'food combining,' consists of five basic rules – the first three are very similar to the recommendations of the monks:

1   The Monks' Advice: *They were vegetarians but ate eggs, butter and cheese in sufficient quantities to 'serve certain functions of the brain, body and nervous system'. They had no need of meat, fish or fowl since they are strong and virile from practicing the Rites.* Dr Hay's Advice: Eat vegetables, salads and fruits as the main part of your diet.

2   The Monks' Advice: *You should keep starches, fruits and vegetables separate from meats, fish and fowl. Starches clash with proteins. If you eat bread (starch) with meats, egg or cheese (protein) a reaction is set up in the stomach which not only causes discomfort, but more importantly contributes to a shorter lifespan.* Dr Hay's Advice: Food Combining: Do not eat carbohydrates with proteins and acid fruits at the same meal.

3   The Monks' Advice *By obtaining the full nourishment from the food, less food needs to be eaten overall.* Dr Hay's Advice: Eat proteins, starches and fats in small quantities.

Dr Hay's remaining 'rules' are:

1   Eat only whole grain and unprocessed starches, excluding refined, processed foods such as white flour, white sugar, and margarine.

2   Allow an interval of at least four to four and half hours between meals of different types.

17

VOICES, VORTEXES, AND VITALITY – PART FOUR

Colonel Bradford was speaking before the "Himalaya Club" for the last time before leaving on a tour of the United States and a visit to his native England. He had selected for his subject the things that help youthify a man, regardless of whether or not he practices Rite Number Six. As the Colonel spoke he seemed to be keener, more alert and vigorous and virile than ever before. Upon his return from the Lamasery he had struck me as the acme of perfection; yet since then he had kept right on improving, and even now was making new gains constantly.

"There are several things I want to talk about tonight," began the Colonel, "which I am sure will interest you. The first of them is the human voice. Do you realize that when one has made a study of men's voices he can tell instantly how much masculine vitality a man possesses just by hearing him speak? You have all heard the shrill, piping voice of an old man. Well, when a man's voice begins to take on that high pitch he is in a very deplorable condition. Let me explain.

"The Vortex at the base of the neck has power over the vocal cords. This Vortex and the one in the sex center are connected. Of course, all the Vortexes have a common connection, but these two are geared together, as it were. What affects one affects the other, so that when a man's voice is high his manly vitality is low. (I am not speaking of Tenor voices.)

"Now all that is necessary to speed up these two Vortexes, along with the others, is to practice the Five Rites. However, one does not have to wait until these Vortexes are increased in speed by the use of the Five Rites, but can raise their speed of vibration with a special method that works very well. This particular practice is easy. It consists of simply putting forth an effort to keep the voice masculine; not allowing it to become high, shrill, or piping. Listen to men with good low voices and become conscious of how a real man's voice sounds. Then whenever you talk, keep the voice down to the masculine vibration.

"Real old men will find this to be quite a little task; but it brings results. The first thing you know the lowered voice will speed up the Vortex in the base of the throat. That will speed up the Vortex in the sex center, which will improve the man in masculine energy, and this again will cause the Vortex in the throat to speed up. The adolescent boy whose voice is changing is experiencing the same thing. The Two Vortexes are speeding up. In this case it is usually caused by the Vortex in the procreative center being speeded up by nature. But anything that will speed up the Vortex in the throat will cause its companion Vortex immediately below to increase speed.

"There are a number of young men who are robust and virile now who will not remain that way long. This is due to the fact that their particular voice, for several reasons I haven't the time to explain now, never came down to the masculine pitch. But these young men, as well as the old ones, can definitely get results of a very wonderful nature by consciously lowering their voices. In the young men it will mean prolonged virility; in the older men, renewed virility.

"Some time ago I came across a quite splendid voice exercise. Like all other potent things it is very simple. Whenever you are by yourself or where there is sufficient noise to drown your voice so that you will not annoy others, practice saying in low tones, partly through the nose:

"Me - me - me - me - e - e - e - e - e - e - e - e – e."

"Repeat it time and again. When you get it down quite low, try it in a small room, like the bath room. You can often make the room hum with your voice. Then try to get the same effect in a larger room. Of course, listening to this vibration of your voice is not entirely necessary; but often the vibration will cause the other Vortexes in the body to speed up, especially the one in the sex center and the two in the head.

"The 'Me - me - e - e - e -' exercise is a good one, but you can use to good advantage other vowels, also. 'Mo mo - o - o - o - o' as well as 'Ma - ma- ma - a - a - a', and 'Mu - mu- mu- u- u- u- u' are good. Like the e's on 'me', and the o's in 'Mo', the a's in 'Ma' and the u's in 'Mu' are drawn out very long as a single sound and not as so many short ones. Each of the vowel sounds should be started with 'M', and the 'M' should be repeated with the vowel three or four times, then draw out the vowel into a long one. Always start with the 'Me - me - me - e - e - e - e' exercise and end with the 'Mu - mu - mu - u - u - u - u' exercise. Start with the first and repeat it twenty-five times, then go on to the others — each twenty-five times. Some students get the best results from the use of the 'Me me - me - e - e - e' practice only.

"In old women, the voice also becomes shrill and should be toned down. Of course, a woman's voice naturally is higher than a man's. If she should get it down as low as a man's, it would not be beneficial at all to her. It would speed up the Two Vortexes - the one in the throat and its companion, so as to cause her to act, look, think, and talk mannishly. By the same token, a mannish woman could wonderfully improve herself by raising her voice to the level of a normal woman's.

"I have known of men with high voices who partook of so much alcoholic beverages that they developed 'whiskey' voices - low and growling. To their amazement they began to become virile again. Usually they attributed their good fortune to intemperance or to a certain brand of whiskey, but neither intemperance nor whiskey did anything for them directly.

"What happened was that the vocal cords were irritated and therefore inflamed and swollen. This lowered the voice and raised the speed of the Vortex in the throat, which in turn, raised the vibrations of the Vortex in the masculine center below, and brought about the renewed masculine vitality.

"Now," said the Colonel, after pausing a moment, "I want to speak on one more subject, which could be entitled 'Putting off the old man.' Lowering the voice and speeding up the Vortexes certainly has a lot to do in eliminating the 'old man' within us, but there are other things which help to make us much younger even though they do not directly affect the Vortexes. If it were possible suddenly to take a man out of a decrepit old body and place him in a brand-new youthful one about 25 years of age, I am confident that the old man he had allowed himself to become would cause him to remain old in most of his ways. It is true that he would perk up a bit around the ladies; outside of that I think he would remain old.

"Getting old, of course, is brought about first by a lack or a complete absence of manly virility. But that is not the only cause. The world is full of old men around 60 who get a certain dubious pleasure out of acting old. This is all wrong. Regardless of whether a man has full vitality at the present time or not, he should do everything possible to eliminate the 'old man' that has crept within him. He must be dislodged and rooted out. Therefore, gentlemen, from now on get rid of the 'old man' within you. How to do it? It is very simple. Don't do the things old people do. With your new and ever-increasing vitality this should be easy.

"The first thing to do is to straighten up. Stand like a man should. When you first started this class, some of you were so bent over that you looked like question marks; but as vigor returned and spirits became better you began to straighten up. That was fine; but don't stop now. Straighten right on up, start throwing your chest out, pull the stomach and the chin in, and right away you have eliminated 20 years from your appearance and 40 years from your mind. Likewise, eliminate the 'old man' mannerisms. When you walk, know first where you are going; then start out and go there. Don't dog-trot or run, and don't shuffle along, but pick up your feet and stride. Keep one eye on where you are going and the other one on everything you pass.

"At the Himalayan Lamasery there was a man, a European, whom you would have sworn was not over 35 years of age, and who acted like a man of 25 in every respect. This man was over a hundred, and if I told you how much over a hundred you would not believe me.

"Now about your weight. If you are underweight, you can throw off the years by increasing your weight. If you are overweight, which is a splendid sign of old age and senility, you can throw off more years by reducing the weight to normal. Get rid of the enlarged abdomens, too, and you will look 10 years younger immediately.

"Here is something else which should interest all of you. Only two years ago I was as bald as the baldest man here. When vitality started coming back, one of the Lamas told me to massage my scalp good with a piece of butter twice a week. The butter up there was fresh, not a bit of salt in it. I took his advice and massaged my scalp with butter until it soon loosened up.

I did this about one hour after a meal. The food elements in the blood were brought to the scalp by the circulation of the blood. The scalp was so thoroughly massaged that the blood vessels were dilated; the hair roots picked up the necessary nutrition, and the hair grew, as you can plainly see.

"Even though you may not care to become mystics at this time, you can throw many years off your mind, your attitude, and feelings. So start at once. Any effort you put forth will be rewarded, I can assure you. I have given you nothing but simple Rites and practices because the simple things will bring you health, youth, virility, and success when nothing else will.

"It has been a most thrilling thing to see you men change and improve from day to day," concluded the Colonel, "but now you know all there is need for you to know for the present. When you are ready for more information, the teacher will appear. There are others who need this information much more than you gentlemen did and I must be on my way to them."

Of course, we were sorry to see our friend the Colonel depart. But we were glad and thankful for the priceless information he had given us. The thought that the Colonel was soon to help other men like ourselves find "The Fountain of Youth," "The Philosopher's Stone," "The Elixir of Life," thrilled us. Truly, I thought to myself, THE EYE OF REVELATION is upon the world.

Note: *In 1946, Peter Kelder republished 'The Eye of Revelation' with amendments, and a whole new Chapter – containing information on 'Mantram-Mind Magic' and 'The Magic Quality of AUM.'*

This information below is an exact copy of the original – taken from the only known-surviving 1946 edition in the world owned by antiquarian book collector and seller, Jerry Watt (RIP) – and reproduced here with his permission.

1946 EDITION – THE EYE OF REVELATION

by Peter Kelder

"THE EYE OF REVELATION" is an Education and Inspiration Course of Study, and of Practice.

"THE EYE OF REVELATION" is intended for men and women everywhere throughout the Western World, and this regardless of nationality.

'THE EYE OF REVELATION" is intended for the personal use of the purchaser of this Course only. It may not be loaned or given to any other person, except members of one's own, immediate family.

'THE EYE OF REVELATION' is intended only for those who are mentally and physically capable of performing the various exercises or rites contained in this book or monograph. The Author and Publishers are therefore, in no way responsible for the misuse of any of the information which is contained herein.

THE MID-DAY PRESS
1045 Midway Place
Los Angeles 15,
California

MANTRAM-MIND MAGIC – PART FIVE

18

N ow and then the "Himalaya Club" would receive a short but interesting communication from Colonel Bradford. He did not stay long in any one place, and so the "Club" knew that he was traveling about and lecturing before other groups throughout the English-speaking world.

One day the "Himalaya Club" received quite a long letter from the Colonel. It contained additional information, and was intended for all of the members. Probably only the more advanced members would be sufficiently interested in it to put it to use.

The title of the subject was: "Mantram-Mind Magic". The word Mantram, as far as the meaning was concerned, was entirely new to the group, although some of the members vaguely remembered seeing it somewhere in print.

Colonel Bradford's letter explained:

"A Mantram is a 'vocalized instrument of thought'. There is a slight difference between Mantram and Mantra. Usually, Mantram means vocalized thought, while Mantra is an inaudible thought.

"Time and again, each of you has had some word or group of words 'run through your mind'. Sometimes it would be only one word, at other times it would be two words, or a short group of words. Often it would be the name of something, or probably some one's name. When something of such a nature keeps running through your mind it is a Mantra — an inaudible instrument of thought. Just how it got started we haven't the space to go into here, and furthermore it is not important to know the cause at this time.

"The important thing is to take advantage of this subconscious activity, and this can easily be done when you know how. This is how you proceed: The moment you become aware of something running through your mind in the form of definite words (not a tune), vocalize it. Let us say that the thought was 'peace in our time'. Now each time the thought — 'peace in our time' — passes through your mind, vocally repeat the thought and add another one to it like this. 'Peace in our time', means peace, power and plenty for me right now. In this way you take a deep-seated sub-conscious activity and attach to it something of meaning and consequence, and after a while when the subconscious ceases to project its activity into your conscious mind, although it will continue to repeat the thought within itself (this has been proven through the use of hypnotism) it will repeat along with its own your added thought, and instead of repeating over and over again, 'peace in our time', it will repeat 'Peace in our time means peace, power and plenty for me right now'.

"Before too long a time by proceeding in this manner your sub-conscious realm of mind will be so 'galvanized' with the meaning of the new thought that you attached to the sub-conscious thought that the sub-conscious mind will begin to put the thought into practice in your conscious life, and the result will be a quieting of the things that disturb you through the word 'peace', and this regardless of what the disturbing elements might consist.

"Don't try to figure out how the sub-conscious is going to overcome certain obstacles in your life and affairs to bring about peace in your life. The sub-conscious in its way is far more clever than is our conscious realm of mind. The conscious mind is always coming up against stone walls, just can't go any further in that direction, and soon hasn't the energy to attempt to go in any other direction, but not so with the subconscious mind. The sub-conscious is not a reasoning mind and so if it is headed-off in one direction it is not discouraged, doesn't give up, because it knows (feels) that there are ten thousand other directions that it can turn, and at least half of that number will permit it to bring about the desired results in YOUR Life and affairs.

"We said that a Mantram was a vocalized instrument of thought. Use a Mantram whenever you can, because the vocalization of the thought causes you to hear it, and this means an additional impression upon the sub-conscious. The idea is to send just as powerful a suggestion into the sub-conscious realm of mind as possible.

"On the other hand, if we are in close contact with other people, as we are when riding along in a train with fellow passengers sitting all about us and even another in the same seat with us, we can't very well speak out and say 'Peace in our time means peace, power and plenty for me right now'. In such a case I would suggest that we use a Mantra, and quietly think to ourself 'Peace in our time means peace, power and plenty for me right now'. True, it will not be quite as effective, but we still will get splendid results.

"Even after the sub-conscious has ceased projecting such a thought into our conscious mind it is a very fine idea to continue the work for some time to come, and every two or three minutes repeat the suggestion along with the subconscious thought of 'Peace in our time'. The 'peace in our time' of the sub-conscious is the OPEN DOOR to the subconscious, and this 'door' remains open for a considerable time after the thought rises high enough to contact our conscious mind.

"Always make your additions to your sub-conscious thought positive, short, and to the point. We explained about the word 'peace', how it brings about desirable results to you. Well, the word 'power', when taken deep into the sub-consciousness will one day bring about health, strength and vitality in our physical bodies, and not only that, we will find that we are actually becoming much more self-controlled, and dominant mentally.

"The word 'plenty' in our suggestion of course means abundance. You not only want peace, but you want an abundance of peace. You are not satisfied with just a little power in body and mind, you want an abundance of it.

"'Right now' at the end of your affirmation gives the subconscious mind some ideas as to when you want all of this to materialize — N-O-W. You desire that the sub-conscious mind start bringing about the desired changes at once. Not a week, or a month, or a year from now, but get busy and cause them to come into manifestation in your life and affairs now.

"The sub-conscious thought will be anything of a million different thoughts or half-thoughts. Sometimes they are the names or [of?] people; other times, the names of plays you have seen either recently or some time ago; or perhaps they will be the names of stories or books. It doesn't matter what the thought is that persists in running through your mind, just add another one to it and everytime [sic] the thought comes to mind repeat the thought that comes to mind, and then attach your thought — your affirmation -to it.

"A long time ago you probably read the book 'Jane Eyre'', or saw the film version of it. Now, for no apparent reason (although there is a good sub-conscious one) the thought 'Jane Eyre' runs through your mind time and time again. Well, just the moment you become aware of it just repeat it and add a thought to it: 'Jane Eyre' means peace, power and plenty to me right now.

"It is wise to place the word means between the sub-conscious thought and your added thought. This informs the subconsciousness in a very short and definite way YOUR MEANING of 'Jane Eyre'. It is necessary to be very definite with the subconscious mind, for in certain respects it is quite child-like, and it must have definite thoughts if you expect it to do its best work.

"No matter what words or phrases run through your mind — 'peace in our time', 'Jane Eyre', 'Wee Willie Winkle', etc., etc., just add YOUR MEANING to them, and as the subconscious activity withdraws itself into the sub-conscious the thoughts, regardless of what they are, will have YOUR THOUGHT attached to them, and it is your thought that will do the miracles in your subconscious world for you. [sic] Not only in your sub-conscious world but a little later on in your CONSCIOUS or OUTER WORLD.

"By all means make up your own affirmations or autosuggestions to suit yourself. While 'peace, power and plenty right now' is good, there is probably something else that you need more than these three. Whatever it is, make it into an affirmation and hook it onto your sub-conscious Mantra to be drawn deep into your sub-conscious world, and put to work.

"Some folks have a sub-conscious mind that is very close to the surface of the conscious mind, and the result is, never a week passes but what they have some subconscious thought running through their conscious mind time and again. If you are one of these people, then about once a week you'll be able to give your sub-conscious realm of mind a very excellent treatment of suggestions or affirmations.

"There are other folks whose sub-conscious is not 'located' so near to the conscious mind and, they seldom if ever have a thought run through their minds hour upon hour or even for a few minutes. These folks, however, can induce the sub-conscious to come to the surface with a thought to which an affirmation can be added.

"Just a catchy little phrase like 'Wee Willie Winkle', if thought to one's self for a short period of time will in most instances cause the sub-conscious to open the door between itself and the conscious mind, and every few seconds repeat 'Wee Willie Winkle', and after a little of this (do not begin too soon) start adding whatever you desire 'Wee Willie Winkle' to mean.

"The sub-conscious realm of mind is a very wonderful 'creation' and it is not half as hard to get it to work with you as to get you to work with it. In fact, the sub-conscious takes great delight in working with you in accomplishing anything that you desire. Desire is a very strong force, and when you use desire to induce the sub-conscious to bring about certain desirable results in your life, it will actually be thrilled to work with you, to actually go out and get the things that you want, to cause the desires of your heart to be realized or materialized.

"This is something that each of you should know: The sub-conscious realm of mind cannot feel pain or sorrow or grief. None of these feelings or emotions are unpleasant to it, would be a better way of stating the matter. Your pain is a thrilling sensation to the sub-conscious. Your joy, enthusiasm, zeal and fervor, also are thrilling sensations to your sub-conscious mind, but as misery is much easier for each one of us to experience than is joy, quite naturally the only real pleasure the sub-conscious gets, and it is a joy-loving 'creature', is from our pain, sorrow and misery, and quite naturally it brings about these unpleasant things in our lives 'thinking' that we get as much pleasure from them as does 'it' — the sub-conscious mind.

"Once we convince the sub-consciousness that we get our big thrills out of the joyous things of life, the subconscious will flood our lives with the thrilling things instead of the miserable things of life.

19

THE MAGIC QUALITY OF AUM

" To a person who doesn't know English, an affirmation such as 'peace, power and plenty right now' wouldn't mean a thing to his sub-conscious mind, unless it was translated into his own language, and he could use words that he was highly familiar with which meant 'peace, power and plenty right now'.

"I mention this because certain teachers from the East have given out certain affirmations which are very fine to people who know the language of the East. But these affirmations are absolutely worthless to English-speaking people because they do not know the meaning of the words or phrases. Even if they have been told the meaning, the words are still just so much jargon to the sub-conscious, and the result is, no good is accomplished. The subconscious is a wonderful thing, but it cannot possibly use thoughts that are enshrouded in foreign words unless these words are <u>completely familiar to you</u>.

"There is one exception, however — a word that comes from the East which has a magical effect upon the subconscious as well as upon the brain and nervous system. This word is 'aum'. The value of the word is not in its meaning but in its vibration. Thus, anyone using it for vibratory purposes, regardless of which particular language of earth [sic] he speaks, will receive a special benefit from it; that is, of course, if he is ready for a high and powerful vibration. Nothing is good or beneficial if its vibration is so great that it is wholly out of harmony with a lesser vibration.

"This particular word — aum — when vibrated correctly, has a very powerful stimulating effect upon the pineal gland, but, the pineal gland should not be stimulated into great action if the life a person is leading is not on a high plane. A person should be sufficiently high in his vibrations through right living that he is beyond the use of habit-forming drugs, which include alcohol and nicotine in any and all forms.

"One's diet should be minus, to a considerable extent (but not entirely), fats of all kinds but especially lard. Meat is permissible in sensible and limited quantities, but <u>pork in any form should be dispensed with</u>. A small amount of butter is permissible. White sugar as well as all foods containing large quantities of white sugar should be used sparingly. Honey and natural sweets can be used instead and even they should not be over-indulged in. They are too sugar [sic], and sugar is a first-cousin to alcohol, and alcohol is completely OUT when one is attempting to travel the path of the thrilling higher vibrations.

"Starches, too, are detrimental unless they are well masticated — practically digested in the mouth — then they are no longer harmful if taken in sensible quantities.

"The average, normal man consumes about two quarts of water each twenty-four hours. A woman weighing less naturally consumes less liquid. The consumption of water should be increased considerably. A man should increase the intake of water from two quarts per day to three, and a woman should increase her consumption of liquid from one quart per day to one and a half. Even a little more for both men and women would be still better. However, the increased amount of water should not be made all at once, but over a period of at

CHAPTER 19 *The Magic Quality of AUM*

least two months, and of course no change at all in the amount of liquid if a person is ailing physically, without permission from their physician.

"The increased use of water should take place first, and for at least a month, then one can use the Aum-Vibration Rite for good results.

"The 'au' in AUM is pronounced 'ah'. It is pronounced through the mouth and is drawn out for about <u>five seconds</u>, then the mouth is closed (not suddenly) and the 'm' is hummed out through the nose (either nostril) for <u>ten seconds</u>.

"After a breath or two, then do the 'au-m-m-m-m-m' again. Three or four times in succession is quite sufficient. Do not overdo a good thing. Stop the moment you begin to feel dizzy. After an hour or so perform the 'aum's' again several times. At first never more than ten times even though no sign of any dizziness has become manifest. Too much pineal stimulation for a beginner is not a positive procedure.

"The best position to take for this Rite is to sit in an easy chair and completely relax. Don't slouch down so that your head will thrust forward and cramp your vocal cords. It is necessary to get a good clear tone both through the mouth and through the nose, and if you are in a cramped position you cannot do this.

"One can even lie flat on the back on a comfortable bed or divan and perform this Rite to splendid advantage. The pillow should be removed so that one can get the head far enough back in order that the vocal cords will not be cramped.

"Don't fill the lungs bursting full of air, but amply sufficient to do the Aum-Vibration for fifteen seconds (five seconds through the mouth — ten seconds through the nose) without being completely out of breath at the end of the 15 seconds.

"Like in the Mantra and Mantram Rites, you can use an affirmation in this Mantram-Aum Rite to splendid advantage.

"You will remember that in the Mantra Rite you repeat your affirmation mentally. In the Mantram Rite you repeat the affirmation vocally. This one is a combination of both of the other Rites. While you are vocalizing 'ah' in aum for five seconds you <u>hold the mind quiet</u>, then while you are intoning the 'm' through the nose for ten seconds <u>you repeat your affirmation mentally several times</u>.

"It is best not to use this Rite and the previous one at the same time. Use this one when the mind is free from any subconscious thoughts running through it.

"Also: It is best to prepare your affirmation before you begin to practice the Aum Rite, so you will know exactly what to suggest. Be sure that it contains exactly that which you wish to become or that which you desire. Be absolutely certain that the affirmation does not contain any negative thoughts or words, in this way you will not build into your sub-consciousness anything of a detrimental character.

"Always remember that while you are humming the 'm' in <u>aum</u> through the nose (mouth closed) you, with your mental affirmation, are making a powerful impression on your subconscious mind, so powerful in fact that your words and your thoughts are being permanently etched upon it, and for this reason you most certainly do not want anything negative in your affirmation. If you do, eventually it will come to the surface mind, and you will have lost all the good which you could otherwise have accomplished.

"This Rite is intended for older people only. It most certainly is not to be used by persons under twenty-one years of age. It is intended for mature men and women. Especially those who have not found life a bed of roses. It is for those who wish to 'reclaim the years that the locusts have eaten'.

"The Illuminati — the Wise Men of old — have all used this unusual form of Mantra or Mantram for raising the vibration of not only their minds and brains, but their physical bodies as well. The Rite has a most beneficial effect on all of the old-age-producing causes in the physical body — by eliminating them, of course. Quite naturally if we refuse to eliminate any of the known old-age producers in mind and body we can not expect to get thrilling results from this particular Rite. But as causes for old age and senility are eliminated we can rest assured that the vibrations of our minds and bodies will be increased, and then we shall go forward to youth of mind and youth of body, and there is nothing more thrilling than a <u>mature</u> young mind in a renewed body.

"One reason why older people make so much better progress, once they start to increase their vibrations than do men and women one-half or even one-third of their age, is due to the fact that they have finally learned that the materialistic world is just a make-shift, make-believe existence, and any joys found in it are as fleeting as dry leaves in a windstorm. They know that the Great Thrills of Life are not found in the outer world, but in the Inner World — in their INNER WORLD. And, once they begin to experience the thrill of the higher vibrations working in their minds and bodies, nothing could ever induce them to go back into the senseless lives they lived before they ever heard of an Inner World.

"The Eye of Revelation is upon you. Great days are ahead for all of us, and this regardless of present conditions or circumstances. Begin anew right where you are, and even though most of you have made gratifying accomplishments, these are as nothing in comparison to the thrilling things that are just a short distance ahead of you."

T5T ADDITIONAL INFORMATION

Aum, also known as "OM," is believed to be the first sound heard from the creator at the beginning of the universe. It is said that this primordial sound is the original sound that contains all other sounds, all words, all languages, and all mantras.

A mantra assists your mind to focus when it is scattered. When you chant a mantra, it produces a powerful vibration that can eventually still all other vibrations, although it takes a lot of practice to achieve this. The purpose of a mantra is to produce a state by which you are able to vibrate at the same rate as the energy and spiritual state produced by and contained within the mantra.

Om is commonly chanted at the beginning and end of a yoga class to attune yourself to the universal consciousness. It allows us to experience our connection or reflection as part of the whole. It can be chanted at any other suitable time, at a length to be determined by the individual chanter, which meets his or her level of total comfort, provided it does not strain the lungs. According to Hindu scriptures, the highest experience in life is to hear the sound of OM in deep silence. The repetition of OM is said to generate the mystical power that can lead your mind into deep meditation and finally into the state of higher consciousness known as Samadhi (bliss).

To chant AUM, you begin with a deep breath. In an effortless single out-breath, the sound A originates in the navel, then rises to the throat with the U, opens the fontanelle at the top of the head, and ends with M, which rolls over the tongue with the lips closed at the final point. At the beginning of the chant, there is an expansion outwards, which ends with a contraction inwards at the conclusion of the M sound. Then repeat again and again as desired.

20

CHOOSING THE RIGHT METHOD FOR YOU

For those who have maintained their fitness through yoga, Pilates or other sports, the T5T method boosts the benefits of the Rites by increasing the strength of the core muscles and the responsiveness of your breathing muscles. This enhances your performance and endurance in all your other sporting activities. Furthermore, developing strong core muscles helps prevent injury and provides a strong foundation for attempting more advanced postures or exercises.

Fit or not, I highly recommend you follow Colonel Bradford's advice by beginning with just three repetitions of each movement in your first week, then adding two per day per week for ten weeks until you will be performing the required 21 repetitions. There are changes to your balance system and energy system that your body needs time to adjust to. Building up repetitions too quickly can create a detox effect as well as a degree of dizziness or nausea. By gradually increasing your repetitions these side-effects can be improved or avoided altogether.

Remember this isn't just physical exercise – the true purpose of the Rites as described by Kelder is:

> "The body has seven centers, which, in English, could be called Vortexes. These are kind of magnetic centers. They revolve at great speed in the healthy body, but when

slowed down – well that is just another name for old age, ill-health, and senility. These spinning centers of activity extend beyond the flesh in the healthy individual, but in the old, weak, senile person they hardly reach the surface, except in the knees. The quickest way to regain health, youth, and vitality is to start these magnetic centers spinning again. There are but five practices that will do this. Any one of them will be helpful, but all five are required to get glowing results. These five exercises are really not exercises at all, in the physical culture sense. The Lamas think of them as 'Rites' and so instead of calling them exercises or practices, we too, shall call them 'Rites'."

~ **Peter Kelder,** *The Eye of Revelation.*

The following questionnaire will help you get clear on what you need before starting *The Five Tibetan Rites.*

THINGS TO BE CONSIDERED BEFORE LEARNING THE RITES

Are you currently doing very little exercise?	YES/NO
Have you ever practiced yoga before?	YES/NO
Have you suffered from back pain or neck pain in the past?	YES/NO
Have you seen any therapist for back or neck pain in the past?	YES/NO
Is one side of your body (or one limb) noticeably stronger than the other?	YES/NO
Have you noticed any muscular weakness in any part of your body?	YES/NO
Have you noticed any stiffness in any part of your body?	YES/NO
Do you find it an effort to maintain an upright stance when sitting or standing? Do you slouch?	YES/NO
Do you hold tension in your shoulders and upper back?	YES/NO
Weak or inflexible wrists. Do you find it a bit of a struggle to unscrew jars/bottles etc.?	YES/NO
Do you find it difficult to turn your neck around sufficiently when reversing your car?	YES/NO
Are you overweight?	YES/NO
Are you largely sedentary? You spend most of your time sitting in front of a desk or relaxing at home?	YES/NO
Are you at a point where you think you had better 'do' something now, before it is too late?	YES/NO

MORE YES ANSWERS THAN NO?

Fit or Relatively Fit?

Is core stability part of your workout?	YES/NO
Are you able to identify and isolate each core muscle; the pelvic floor, transversus abdominis & multifidus muscles.	YES/NO
Do you know when or if you incorrectly use your obliques to stabilise rather than your core muscles?	YES/NO
Do you know how to establish and maintain neutral spine and neutral pelvis, whilst keeping your head and neck in line with your spine?	YES/NO
How good is your breathing? Apart from being good at pranayama, do you know what natural, full breathing should feel like? Do you have tension in your breathing? How are your stress levels? Do you find yourself breathing rapidly in the upper chest, holding your breath, yawning or sighing?	YES/NO

Having completed this questionnaire, you should have a better idea of which method is best for you. Most people begin practicing by following the instructions in this book, but if you want more detailed explanations and alternatives, you might prefer to learn the T5T version. Regardless of which method you use, you will find answers to frequently asked questions, resources, information, and interesting articles on my T5T website.

ABOUT THE AUTHOR

Carolinda Witt is an award-winning author who lives in Sydney.

Carolinda keeps herself fit and healthy by practicing The Five Tibetan Rites, which she began in 2000. She has taught the Rites to over 50,000 people all over the world through her books, online training course, DVD, and workshops - and attributes them to her youthful appearance and energetic outlook.

Carolinda knows the solutions to the common problems beginners experience when learning the Rites - and how to fix them.

If you find the simple instructions in *The Eye of Revelation* are not detailed enough for you to learn from, then please check out the T5T website for more comprehensive information.

OTHER BOOKS, VIDEOS & ONLINE TRAINING COURSES BY THIS AUTHOR

Visit your favorite online retailer or the *T5T.com* website to discover other items by Carolinda Witt.

1) ONLINE TRAINING COURSE

- *Workbook & Video Series*

2) PAPERBACK & KINDLE BOOKS

1. *The Illustrated Five Tibetan Rites* – (UnMind Pty Ltd)
2. *T5T: The Five Tibetan Exercise Rites* – (Lantern/Penguin, Australia). Out of print.
3. *The 10-Minute Rejuvenation Plan* – (Clarkson Potter, NY). Out of print.

3) DVD

- *The Five Tibetans DVD* – UnMind Pty Ltd.

4) *Award-Winning Book,* **Double Agent Celery: MI5's Crooked Hero** - (Pen & Sword Books, UK). Carolinda recounts the incredible story of her spy grandfather, Walter Dicketts, who was sent into Nazi Germany by MI5 to infiltrate the Abwehr in the guise of a traitor and bring back crucial secrets. Interrogated, drugged, and plied with alcohol, Dicketts survived to tell the tale. Sadly, Carolinda's mother died without ever knowing his name.

CONNECT WITH CAROLINDA WITT

I really appreciate you reading my book! Here are my social media coordinates:

1. Connect with other Five Tibetans practitioners and me on *Facebook*

2. Visit my websites: *www.T5T.com* and *carolindawitt.com*

3. Subscribe to my *blog*

Printed in Great Britain
by Amazon

87375538R00068